Percy Jackson's
GREEK
GODS

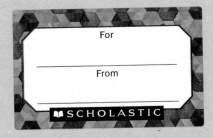

For

_____

From

_____

SCHOLASTIC

RICK RIORDAN

PERCY JACKSON'S GREEK GODS

WITH A FULL-COLOR
INSERT OF ARTWORK BY
JOHN ROCCO

SCHOLASTIC INC.

ISBN 978-1-338-03632-9

12 11 10 9 8 7 6 5 4 3   16 17 18 19 20 21

Printed in the U.S.A.   40

First Scholastic printing, February 2016

To my father, Rick Riordan, Sr., who read me my first book of mythology
—R.R.

TABLE OF CONTENTS

INTRODUCTION

I HOPE I'M GETTING EXTRA CREDIT FOR THIS.

A publisher in New York asked me to write down what I know about the Greek gods, and I was like, "Can we do this anonymously? Because I don't need the Olympians mad at me again."

But if it helps you to know your Greek gods, and survive an encounter with them if they ever show up in your face, then I guess writing all this down will be my good deed for the week.

If you don't know me, my name is Percy Jackson. I'm a modern-day demigod——a half-god, half-mortal son of Poseidon—but I'm not going to say much about myself. My story has already been written down in some books that are total fiction (wink, wink) and I am just a character from the story (*cough*—yeah, right—*cough*).

Just go easy on me while I'm telling you about the gods, all right? There's like forty bajillion different versions of the myths, so don't be all *Well, I heard it a different way, so you're WRONG!*

I'm going to tell you the versions that make the most sense to me. I promise I didn't make any of this up. I got all these stories straight from the Ancient Greek and Roman dudes who wrote them down in the first place. Believe me, I couldn't make up stuff this weird.

So here we go. First I'll tell you how the world got made. Then I'll run down a list of gods and give you my two cents about each of them. I just hope I don't make them so mad they incinerate me before I—

AGGHHHHHHHHHH!

Just kidding. Still here.

Anyway, I'll start with the Greek story of creation, which by the way, is seriously *messed up*. Wear your safety glasses and your raincoat. There will be blood.

THE BEGINNING
AND STUFF

IN THE BEGINNING, I wasn't there. I don't think the
Ancient Greeks were, either. Nobody had a pen and paper
to take notes, so I can't vouch for what follows, but I can
tell you it's what the Greeks *thought* happened.

At first, there was pretty much nothing. A lot of nothing.

The first god, if you can call it that, was Chaos—a gloomy,
soupy mist with all the matter in the cosmos just drifting
around. Here's a fact for you: *Chaos* literally means the *Gap*, and
we're not talking about the clothing store.

Eventually Chaos got less chaotic. Maybe it got bored with
being all gloomy and misty. Some of its matter collected and
solidified into the earth, which unfortunately developed a living personality. She called herself Gaea, the Earth Mother.

Now Gaea *was* the actual earth—the rocks, the hills, the valleys, the whole enchilada. But she could also take on humanlike

I

form. She liked to walk across the earth—which was basically walking across herself—in the shape of a matronly woman with a flowing green dress, curly black hair, and a serene smile on her face. The smile hid a nasty disposition. You'll see that soon enough.

After a long time alone, Gaea looked up into the misty nothing above the earth and said to herself: "You know what would be good? A sky. I could really go for a sky. And it would be nice if he was also a handsome man I could fall in love with, because I'm kind of lonely down here with just these rocks."

Either Chaos heard her and cooperated, or Gaea simply willed it to happen. Above the earth, the sky formed—a protective dome that was blue in the daytime and black at night. The sky named himself Ouranos—and, yeah, that's another spelling for Uranus. There's pretty much no way you can pronounce that name without people snickering. It just sounds *wrong*. Why he didn't choose a better name for himself—like Deathbringer or José—I don't know, but it might explain why Ouranos was so cranky all the time.

Like Gaea, Ouranos could take human shape and visit the earth—which was good, because the sky is way up there and long-distance relationships never work out.

In physical form, he looked like a tall, buff guy with long-ish dark hair. He wore only a loincloth, and his skin changed color—sometimes blue with cloudy patterns across his muscles, sometimes dark with glimmering stars. Hey, Gaea dreamed him up to look like that. Don't blame me. Sometimes you'll see pictures of him holding a zodiac wheel, representing all the constellations that pass through the sky over and over for eternity.

Anyway, Ouranos and Gaea got married.

Happily ever after?

Not exactly.

Part of the problem was that Chaos got a little creation-happy. It thought to its misty, gloomy self: Hey, Earth and Sky. That was fun! I wonder what else I can make.

Soon it created all sorts of other problems—and by that I mean gods. Water collected out of the mist of Chaos, pooled in the deepest parts of the earth, and formed the first seas, which naturally developed a consciousness—the god Pontus.

Then Chaos really went nuts and thought: I know! How about a dome like the sky, but at the *bottom* of the earth! That would be awesome!

So another dome came into being beneath the earth, but it was dark and murky and generally not very nice, since it was always hidden from the light of the sky. This was Tartarus, the Pit of Evil; and as you can guess from the name, when he developed a godly personality, he didn't win any popularity contests.

The problem was, both Pontus and Tartarus liked Gaea, which put some pressure on her relationship with Ouranos.

A bunch of other primordial gods popped up, but if I tried to name them all we'd be here for weeks. Chaos and Tartarus had a kid together (don't ask how; I don't know) called Nyx, who was the embodiment of Night. Then Nyx, somehow all by herself, had a daughter named Hemera, who was Day. Those two never got along because they were as different as . . . well, you know.

According to some stories, Chaos also created Eros, the god of procreation . . . in other words, mommy gods and daddy gods having lots of little baby gods. Other stories claim Eros was the son of Aphrodite. We'll get to her later. I don't know which version is true, but I *do* know Gaea and Ouranos started having kids—with *very* mixed results.

First, they had a batch of twelve—six girls and six boys called the Titans. These kids looked human, but they were much taller and more powerful. You'd figure twelve kids would be enough for anybody, right? I mean, with a family that big, you've basically got your own reality TV show.

Plus, once the Titans were born, things started to go sour with Ouranos and Gaea's marriage. Ouranos spent a lot more time hanging out in the sky. He didn't visit. He didn't help with the kids. Gaea got resentful. The two of them started fighting. As the kids grew older, Ouranos would yell at them and basically act like a horrible dad.

A few times, Gaea and Ouranos tried to patch things up. Gaea decided maybe if they had another set of kids, it would bring them closer. . . .

I know, right? Bad idea.

She gave birth to triplets. The problem: these new kids defined the word UGLY. They were as big and strong as Titans, except hulking and brutish and in desperate need of a body wax. Worst of all, each kid had a single eye in the middle of his forehead.

Talk about a face only a mother could love. Well, Gaea loved these guys. She named them the Elder Cyclopes, and eventually they would spawn a whole race of other, lesser Cyclopes. But that was much later.

When Ouranos saw the Cyclops triplets, he freaked. "These cannot be my kids! They don't even look like me!"

4

"They *are* your children, you deadbeat!" Gaea screamed back. "Don't you dare leave me to raise them on my own!"

"Don't worry, I won't," Ouranos growled.

He stormed off and came back with thick chains made from the night sky's pure darkness. He bound up the Cyclopes and tossed them into Tartarus, which was the only part of creation where Ouranos wouldn't have to look at them.

Harsh, right?

Gaea screamed and wailed, but Ouranos refused to release the Cyclopes. No one else dared to oppose his orders, because by this time he was getting a reputation as a pretty scary dude.

"I am king of the universe!" he bellowed. "How could I *not* be? I am literally above everything else."

"I hate you!" Gaea wailed.

"Bah! You will do as I say. I am the first and best of the primordial gods."

"I was born *before* you!" Gaea protested. "You wouldn't even be here if I didn't—"

"Don't test me," he snarled. "I've got plenty more chains of darkness."

As you can guess, Gaea threw a total earthquake fit, but she didn't see what else she could do. Her first kids, the Titans, were almost adults now. They felt bad for Mom. They didn't like their dad much either—Gaea was always bad-mouthing him, with good reason—but the Titans were scared of Ouranos and felt helpless to stop him.

I have to keep it together for the kids, Gaea thought. Maybe I should give it one more try with Ouranos.

She arranged a nice romantic evening—candles, roses, soft music. They must have rekindled some of the old magic. A few months later, Gaea gave birth to one more set of triplets.

As if she needed more proof that her marriage to Ouranos was dead . . .

The new kids were even more monstrous than the Cyclopes. Each one had a hundred arms all around his chest like sea urchin spines, and fifty teeny, tiny heads clustered on his shoulders. It didn't matter to Gaea. She loved their little faces—all hundred and fifty of them. She called the triplets the Hundred-Handed Ones. She'd barely had time to give them names, though, when Ouranos marched over, took one look at them, and snatched them from Gaea's arms. Without a word, he wrapped them in chains and tossed them into Tartarus like bags of recycling.

Clearly, the sky dude had issues.

Well, that was pretty much it for Gaea. She wailed and moaned and caused so many earthquakes that her Titan kids came running to see what was wrong.

"Your father is a complete _____!"

I don't know what she called him, but I have a feeling that's when the first cuss words were invented.

She explained what had happened. Then she raised her arms and caused the ground to rumble beneath her. She summoned the hardest substance she could find from her earthy domain, shaped it with her anger, and created the first weapon ever made—a curved iron blade about three feet long. She fixed it to a wooden handle made from a nearby tree branch, then showed her invention to the Titans.

"Behold, my children!" she said. "The instrument of my revenge. I will call it a scythe!"

The Titans muttered among themselves: *What is that for? Why is it curved? How do you spell* scythe?

"One of you needs to step up!" Gaea cried. "Ouranos isn't worthy to be the king of the cosmos. One of you will kill him and take his place."

The Titans looked pretty uncomfortable.

"So . . . explain this whole *killing* thing," said Oceanus. He was the oldest Titan boy, but he mostly hung out in the far reaches of the sea with the primordial water god, whom he called Uncle Pontus. "What does it mean, to kill?"

"She wants us to exterminate our dad," Themis guessed. She was one of the smartest girls, and she immediately got the concept of punishing someone for a crime. "Like, make him not exist anymore."

"Is that even possible?" asked her sister Rhea. "I thought we were all immortal."

Gaea snarled in frustration. "Don't be cowards! It's very simple. You take this sharp pointy blade and you cut your dad into small pieces so he can't bother us again. Whichever of you does this will be the ruler of the universe! Also, I will make you those cookies you used to like, with the sprinkles."

Now, in modern times, we have a word for this sort of behavior. We call it *psycho.*

Back then, the rules of behavior were a lot looser. Maybe you'll feel better about your own relatives, knowing that the first family in creation was also the first *dysfunctional* family.

The Titans started mumbling and pointing to each other like, "Hey, you'd be good at killing Dad."

"Uh, no, I think *you* should do it."

"I'd love to kill Dad, honestly, but I've got this thing I have to do, so—"

"*I'll* do it!" said a voice from the back.

The youngest of the twelve shouldered his way forward. Kronos was smaller than his brothers and sisters. He wasn't the smartest or the strongest or the fastest. But he *was* the most power-hungry. I suppose when you're the youngest of twelve kids, you're always looking for ways to stand out and get noticed. The youngest Titan loved the idea of taking over the world, especially if it meant being the boss of all his siblings. The offer of cookies with sprinkles didn't hurt, either.

Kronos stood about nine feet tall, which was runty for a Titan. He didn't look as dangerous as some of his brothers, but the kid was crafty. He'd already gotten the nickname "the Crooked One" among his siblings, because he would fight dirty in their wrestling matches and was never where you expected him to be.

He had his mother's smile and dark curly hair. He had his father's cruelty. When he looked at you, you could never tell if he was about to punch you or tell you a joke. His beard was kind of unnerving, too. He was young for a beard, but he'd already started growing his whiskers into a single spike that jutted from his chin like the beak of a raven.

When Kronos saw the scythe, his eyes gleamed. He wanted that iron blade. Alone among his siblings, he understood how much damage it could cause.

And as for killing his dad—why not? Ouranos barely noticed him. Neither did Gaea, for that matter. His parents probably didn't even know his name.

Kronos hated being ignored. He was tired of being the smallest and wearing all those stupid Titan hand-me-downs.

"I'll do it," he repeated. "I'll chop up Dad."

"My favorite son!" Gaea cried. "You are *awesome!* I knew I could count on you, uh . . . which one are you again?"

"Kronos." He managed to keep his smile. Hey, for a scythe, cookies, and a chance to commit murder, Kronos could hide his true feelings. "I will be honored to kill for you, Mother. But we'll have to do it my way. First, I want you to trick Ouranos into visiting you. Tell him you're sorry. Tell him it's all your fault and you're going to cook him a fancy dinner to apologize. Just get him here tonight and act like you still love him."

"Ugh!" Gaea gagged. "Are you crazy?"

"Just pretend," Kronos insisted. "Once he's in human form and sitting next to you, I'll jump out and attack him. But I'll need some help."

He turned to his siblings, who were all suddenly very interested in their own feet.

"Look, guys," said Kronos, "if this goes bad, Ouranos is going to take revenge on *all* of us. We can't have any mistakes. I'll need four of you to hold him down and make sure he doesn't escape back into the sky before I finish killing him."

The others were silent. They were probably trying to picture their shrimpy little brother Kronos taking on their huge violent dad, and they weren't liking the odds.

"Oh, come on!" Kronos chided. "I'll do the actual slicing and dicing. Four of you just need to hold him. When I'm king, I'll reward those four! I'll give them each a corner of the earth to rule—north, south, east, and west. One-time offer. Who's with me?"

The girls were too wise to get involved in murder. They made their excuses and quickly left. The oldest son, Oceanus, chewed his thumb nervously. "I have to get back to the sea, for some, uh, aquatic stuff. Sorry . . ."

That left only four of Kronos's brothers—Koios, Iapetus, Krios, and Hyperion.

Kronos smiled at them. He took the scythe from Gaea's hands and tested its point, drawing a drop of golden blood from his own finger. "So, four volunteers! Nice!"

Iapetus cleared his throat. "Uh, actually—"

Hyperion jabbed Iapetus with his elbow. "We're in, Kronos!" he promised. "You can count on us!"

"Excellent," Kronos said, which was the first time an evil genius ever said *excellent*. He told them the plan.

That night, amazingly, Ouranos showed up.

He wandered into the valley where he usually met Gaea and frowned when he saw the sumptuous dinner laid out on the table. "I got your note. Are you serious about making up?"

"Absolutely!" Gaea was dressed in her best green sleeveless dress. Her curly hair was braided with jewels (which were easy for her to get, being the earth), and she smelled of roses and jasmine. She reclined on a sofa in the soft light of the candles and beckoned her husband to come closer.

Ouranos felt underdressed in his loincloth. He hadn't brushed his hair or anything. His nighttime skin was dark and covered with stars, but that probably didn't count as "black tie" for a fancy dinner. He was starting to think he should've at least brushed his teeth.

Was he suspicious? I don't know. Remember, nobody in the history of the cosmos had been lured into an ambush and chopped to pieces before. He was going to be the first. Lucky guy. Also, he got lonely hanging out in the sky so much. His only company was the stars, the air god Aither (who was, in fact, a total airhead), and Nyx and Hemera, mother and daughter, who argued with each other every dawn and dusk.

"So . . ." Ouranos's palms felt sweaty. He'd forgotten how beautiful Gaea could be when she wasn't all yelling up in his face. "You're not angry anymore?"

"Not at all!" Gaea assured him.

"And . . . you're okay with me wrapping our kids in chains and throwing them into the abyss?"

Gaea gritted her teeth and forced a smile. "I am *okay* with it."

"Good," he grunted. "Because those little guys were UGLY."

Gaea patted the couch. "Come sit with me, my husband."

Ouranos grinned and lumbered over.

As soon as he settled in, Kronos whispered from behind the nearest boulder: "Now."

His four brothers jumped out from their hiding places. Krios had disguised himself as a bush. Koios had dug a hole for himself and covered it with branches. Hyperion had tucked himself under the couch (it was a large couch), and Iapetus was attempting to look like a tree with his arms out for branches. For some reason, it had worked.

The four brothers grabbed Ouranos. Each one took an arm or a leg and they wrestled their dad to the ground, stretching him out spread-eagle.

Kronos emerged from the shadows. His iron scythe gleamed in the starlight. "Hello, Father."

"What is the meaning of this?" Ouranos bellowed. "Gaea, tell them to release me!"

"HA!" Gaea rose from her couch. "You gave our children no mercy, my husband, so you deserve no mercy. Besides, who wears a loincloth to a fancy dinner? I am disgusted!"

Ouranos struggled in vain. "How dare you! I am the lord of the cosmos!"

"Not anymore." Kronos raised the scythe.

"Beware! If you do this, uh . . . what was your name again?"

"KRONOS!"

"If you do this, Kronos," said Ouranos, "I will curse you! Someday, your *own* children will destroy you and take your throne, just as you are doing to me!"

Kronos laughed. "Let them try."

He brought down the scythe.

It hit Ouranos right in the . . . well, you know what? I can't even say it. If you're a guy, imagine the most painful place you could possibly be hit.

Yep. That's the place.

Kronos chopped, and Ouranos howled in pain. It was like the most disgusting cheap-budget horror movie you can imagine. Blood was everywhere—except the blood of the gods is golden, and it's called *ichor*.

Droplets of it splattered over the rocks; and the stuff was so powerful that later on, when no one was looking, creatures arose from the ichor—three hissing winged demons called the Furies, the spirits of punishment. They immediately fled into the darkness of Tartarus. Other drops of sky blood fell on fertile soil, where they eventually turned into wild but gentler creatures called *nymphs* and *satyrs*.

Most of the blood just splattered everything. Seriously, those stains were *never* going to come out of Kronos's shirt.

"Well done, brothers!" Kronos grinned ear to ear, his scythe dripping gold.

Iapetus got sick on the spot. The others laughed and patted each other on the back.

"Oh, my children!" Gaea said. "I am so proud! Cookies and punch for everyone!"

Before the celebration, Kronos gathered up the remains of his father in the tablecloth. Maybe because he resented his eldest brother, Oceanus, for not helping with the murder, Kronos toted the stuff to the sea and tossed it in. The blood mixed with the salty water, and . . . well, you'll see what came from that later.

Now you're going to ask, *Okay, so if the sky was killed, why do I look up and still see the sky?*

Answer: *I dunno.*

My guess is that Kronos killed Ouranos's physical form, so the sky god could no longer appear on the earth and claim kingship. They basically exiled him into the air. So he's not dead, exactly; but now he can't do anything but be the harmless dome over the world.

Anyway, Kronos returned to the valley, and all the Titans had a party.

Gaea named Kronos lord of the universe. She made him a cool one-of-a-kind collector's edition golden crown and everything. Kronos kept his promise and gave his four helpful brothers control over the four corners of the earth. Iapetus became the Titan of the west. Hyperion got the east. Koios took the north, and Krios got the south.

That night, Kronos lifted his glass of nectar, which was the immortals' favorite drink. He tried for a confident smile, since kings should always look confident, though truthfully he was already starting to worry about Ouranos's curse—that someday Kronos's own children would depose him.

In spite of that, he yelled, "My siblings, a toast! We have begun a Golden Age!"

And if you like lots of lying, stealing, backstabbing, and cannibalism, then read on, because it definitely was a Golden Age for all that.

THE GOLDEN AGE OF CANNIBALISM

A T FIRST, KRONOS WASN'T SO BAD. He had to work his way up to being a *complete* slime bucket.

He released the Elder Cyclopes and the Hundred-Handed Ones from Tartarus, which made Gaea happy. The monstrous guys turned out to be useful, too. They had spent all their time in the abyss learning how to forge metal and build with stone (I guess that's pretty much all there was to do), so in gratitude for their freedom, they constructed a massive palace for Kronos on top of Mount Othrys, which back then was the tallest mountain in Greece.

The palace was made from void-black marble. Towering columns and vast halls gleamed in the light of magical torches. Kronos's throne was carved from a solid block of obsidian, inlaid with gold and diamonds—which sounds impressive, but probably wasn't very comfortable. That didn't matter to

Kronos. He could sit there all day, surveying the entire world below him, cackling evilly, "Mine! All mine!"

His five Titan brothers and six Titan sisters didn't argue with him. They had pretty much staked out their favorite territories already—and besides, after seeing Kronos wield that scythe, they didn't want to get on his bad side.

In addition to being king of the cosmos, Kronos became the Titan of time. He couldn't pop around the time stream like Doctor Who or anything, but he *could* occasionally make time slow down or speed up. Whenever you're in an incredibly boring lecture that seems to take forever, blame Kronos. Or when your weekend is *way* too short, that's Kronos's fault, too.

He was especially interested in the destructive power of time. Being immortal, he couldn't believe what a few short years could do to a mortal life. Just for kicks, he used to travel around the world, fast-forwarding the lives of trees, plants, and animals so he could watch them wither and die. He never got tired of that.

As for his brothers, the four who helped with the murder of Ouranos were given the four corners of the earth—which is weird, since the Greeks thought the world was a big flat circle like a shield, so it didn't really *have* corners, but whatever.

Krios was the Titan of the south. He took the ram for his symbol, since the ram constellation rose in the southern sky. His navy blue armor was dotted with stars. Ram's horns jutted from his helmet. Krios was the dark, silent type. He would stand down there at the southern edge of world, watching the constellations and thinking deep thoughts—or maybe he was just thinking he should have requested a more exciting job.

Koios, the Titan of the north, lived at the opposite end of the world (obviously). He was sometimes called Polus, because he controlled the northern pole. This was way before Santa Claus moved in. Koios was also the first Titan to have the gift of prophecy. In fact, *Koios* literally means *question.* He could ask questions of the sky, and sometimes the sky would whisper answers. Creepy? Yes. I don't know if he was communing with the spirit of Ouranos or what, but his glimpses of the future were so useful that other Titans started asking him burning questions like: *What's the weather going to be on Saturday? Is Kronos going to kill me today? What should I wear to Rhea's dance?* That kind of thing. Eventually Koios would pass down the gift of prophecy to his children.

Hyperion, Titan of the east, was the flashiest of the four. Since the light of day came from the east every morning, he called himself the Lord of Light. Behind his back, everybody else called him Kronos Lite, because he did whatever Kronos told him, and was basically like Kronos with half the calories and none of the taste. Anyway, he wore blazing golden armor and was known to burst into flames at random moments, which made him fun at parties.

His counterpart, Iapetus, was more laid-back, being the Titan of the west. A good sunset always makes you want to kick back and chill. Despite that, you didn't want to get this guy mad at you. He was an excellent fighter who knew how to use a spear. *Iapetus* literally means *the Piercer,* and I'm pretty sure he didn't get that name by doing ear-piercings at the mall.

As for the last brother, Oceanus, he took charge of the outer waters that circled the world. That's how the big expanses of water bordering the earth came to be called *oceans.* It could have been worse. If Iapetus had taken over the waters, today we'd be talking about the *Atlantic Iapet* and *sailing the iapet blue*, and that just doesn't have the same ring to it.

Now, before I turn to the six lady Titans, let me get some nasty business out of the way.

See, eventually the guy Titans started thinking, Hey, Dad had Gaea for a wife. Who are *we* going to have for wives? Then they looked at the lady Titans and thought, Hmm . . .

I know. You're screaming, *GROSS! The brothers wanted to marry their own* sisters*?!*

Yeah. I find that pretty disgusting myself, but here's the thing: Titans didn't see family relationships the same way we do.

First off, like I said before, the rules of behavior were a lot looser back then. Also, there weren't many choices when it came to marriage partners. You couldn't simply log into TitanMatch .com and find your perfect soul mate.

Most important, immortals are just *different* from humans. They live forever, more or less. They have cool powers. They have ichor instead of blood and DNA, so they aren't concerned about bloodlines not mixing well. Because of that, they don't see the whole brother-sister thing in the same way. You and the girl you like might have been born of the same mom, but once you grew up and you were both adults, you wouldn't necessarily think of her as your sister anymore.

That's my theory. Or maybe the Titans were all just freaks. I'll let you decide.

Anyway, not *all* the brothers married all the sisters, but here's the rundown.

———————

The oldest girl was Theia. If you wanted her attention, all you had to do was wave something shiny in her face. She *loved* sparkly things and bright scenic views. Every morning she would dance with happiness when daylight returned. She would climb mountains just so she could see for miles around. She would even delve underground and bring out precious gems, using her magic powers to make them gleam and sparkle. Theia is the one who gave gold its luster and made diamonds glitter.

She became the Titan of clear sight. Because she was all about bright and glittery, she ended up marrying Hyperion, the lord of light. As you can imagine, they got along great, though how they got any sleep with Hyperion glowing all night and Theia giggling, "Shiny! Shiny!" I don't know.

Her sister Themis? Totally different. She was quiet and thoughtful and never tried to draw attention to herself, always wearing a simple white shawl over her hair. She realized from an early age that she had a natural sense of right and wrong. She understood what was fair and what wasn't. Whenever she was in doubt, she claimed that she could draw wisdom straight from the earth. I don't think she meant from *Gaea*, though, because Gaea wasn't really hung up on right and wrong.

Anyway, Themis had a good reputation among her brothers and sisters. She could mediate even the worst arguments. She became the Titan of natural law and fairness. She didn't marry any of her six brothers, which just proves how wise she was.

Third sister: Tethys, and I promise this is the last "T" name for the girls, because even *I'm* getting confused. She loved rivers, springs, and fresh running water of any kind. She was very kind, always offering her siblings something to drink, though the others got tired of hearing that the average Titan needs twenty-four large glasses of water a day to stay hydrated. At any rate, Tethys thought of herself as the nursemaid for the whole world, since all living things need to drink. She ended up marrying Oceanus, which was kind of a no-brainer. "Hey, you like water? I like water too! We should totally go out!"

Phoebe, the fourth sister, lived right in the geographic center of the world, which for the Greeks meant the Oracle of Delphi—a sacred spring where you could sometimes hear whispers of the future if you knew how to listen. The Greeks called this place the *omphalos*, literally the belly button of the earth, though they never specified whether it was an innie or an outie.

Phoebe was one of the first people to figure out how to hear the voices of Delphi, but she wasn't a gloomy, mysterious sort of fortune-teller. Her name meant *bright*, and she always looked on the positive side of things. Her prophecies tended to be like fortune cookies—only good stuff. Which was fine, I guess, if you only wanted to hear good news, but not so great if you had a serious problem. Like if you were going to die tomorrow, Phoebe might just tell you, "Oh, um, I foresee that you won't have to worry about your math test next week!"

Phoebe ended up marrying Koios, the northern dude, because he also had the gift of prophecy. Unfortunately, they only saw each other once in a while since they lived very far apart. Bonus fact: much later, Phoebe's grandson, a guy named Apollo, took over the Oracle. Because he inherited her powers, Apollo was sometimes called Phoebus Apollo.

Titan sister five was Mnemosyne—and, man, with my dyslexia I had to spell check that name about twenty times, and it's probably still wrong. Pretty sure it's pronounced NEMO-sign. Anyway, Mnemosyne was born with a photographic memory long before anyone knew what a photograph was. Seriously, she remembered *everything*—her sisters' birthdays, her homework, putting out the garbage, feeding the cats. In some ways, that was good. She kept the family records and never *ever* forgot anything. But in some ways, having her around was a drag, because she would never *let* you forget anything.

That embarrassing thing you did when you were eight years old? Yep, she remembered. That promise you made three years ago that you would pay her back that loan? She remembered.

What was worse, Mnemosyne expected everybody else to have a good memory too. Just to be helpful, she invented letters and writing so the rest of us poor schmucks who didn't have perfect recall could keep permanent records of everything. She became the Titan of memory, especially rote memorization. Next time you have to study for a spelling test or memorize the capitals of all fifty states for no apparent reason, thank Mnemosyne. That kind of assignment was *totally* her idea. None of her fellow Titans wanted to marry her. Go figure.

Finally, there was sister number six: Rhea. Poor Rhea. She was the sweetest and most beautiful of the lady Titans, which of course meant she had the worst luck and the hardest life. Her name either means *flow* or *ease*. Both definitions fit. She always went with the flow, and she totally put people at ease. She would wander the valleys of the earth, visiting her brothers and sisters, talking to the nymphs and satyrs who had sprung from the blood of Ouranos. She loved animals, too. Her favorite was the lion. If you see pictures of Rhea, she almost always has a couple of lions with her, which made it *very* safe for her to walk around, even in the worst neighborhoods.

Rhea became the Titan of motherhood. She adored babies and always helped her sisters during their deliveries. Eventually she would earn the title *the Great Mother* when she had kids of her own. Unfortunately, she had to get married before any of that happened, which is how all the trouble started. . . .

Oh, but everything was so great! What could possibly go wrong?

That's what the Earth Mother Gaea thought. She was so pleased to see her kids in charge of the world, she decided to sink back down into the earth for a while and just be, well . . . the earth. She'd been through a lot. She'd had eighteen kids. She deserved a rest.

She was sure Kronos would take care of things and be a good king forever and ever. (Yeah, right.) So she lay down for a quick nap, which in geological terms meant a few millennia.

Meanwhile, the Titans started having kids of their own, who were second-generation Titans. Oceanus and Tethys, Mr. & Mrs. Water, had a daughter named Klymene, who became the Titan goddess of fame. I'm guessing she was into fame because she grew up at the bottom of the ocean where nothing ever happened. She was *all* about gossip and reading the tabloids and catching up on the latest Hollywood news . . . or she would've been, if Hollywood existed. Like a lot of folks who are obsessed with fame, she headed west. She ended up falling for the Titan of the west, Iapetus.

I know, he was technically her uncle. Disgusting. But like I said before, the Titans were different. My advice is not to think about it too much.

Anyway, Iapetus and Klymene had a son named Atlas, who turned out to be an excellent fighter, and also kind of a jerk. When he grew up, he became Kronos's right-hand man and main enforcer.

Next, Iapetus and Klymene had a son named Prometheus, who was almost as clever as Kronos. According to some legends, Prometheus invented a minor life form you may have heard of—humans. One day he was just messing around at the riverbank, building stuff out of wet clay, when he sculpted a couple of funny-looking figures similar to Titans, only much smaller and easier to smash. Maybe some blood of Ouranos got into the clay, or maybe Prometheus breathed life into the figures on purpose—I don't know. But the clay creatures came to life and became the first two humans.

Did Prometheus get a medal for that? Nah. The Titans looked on humans the way we might look on gerbils. Some Titans thought humans were kind of cute, though they died awfully quick and didn't really serve any purpose. Other Titans thought they were repulsive rodents. Some Titans didn't pay them any attention at all. As for the humans, they mostly just cowered in their caves and scurried around trying not to get stepped on.

The Titans kept having more baby Titans. I won't mention all of them or we'll be here for as long as Gaea napped, but Koios and Phoebe, the prophecy couple, had a girl named Leto, who decided she wanted to be the Titan protector of the young. She was the world's first babysitter. All the dad and mom Titans were really happy to see her.

Hyperion and Theia, Mr. & Mrs. Shiny, had twins named Helios and Selene, who were in charge of the sun and the moon. Makes sense, right? You can't get much shinier than the sun and the moon.

Helios would drive the chariot of the sun across the sky every day, even though it got terrible mileage. Helios thought he looked pretty hot, and he had an annoying habit of calling the sun his "chick magnet."

Selene wasn't quite so flashy. She drove her silver moon chariot across the sky at night and mostly kept to herself, though the one time she *did* fall in love, it was the saddest story ever. But that's for later.

At any rate, one particular Titan wasn't getting married or having kids . . . namely Kronos, the lord of the universe. He just sat on his throne in the palace of Mount Othrys and got very, very grumpy watching everyone else have a good time.

Remember that curse Ouranos warned him about—that someday Kronos's own kids would overthrow him? Kronos couldn't get that out of his head.

At first he told himself, *Well, no biggie. I just won't get married or have kids!*

But it's a pain to be on your own when everyone around you is settling down and starting families. Kronos had earned the throne fair and square, but that curse took all the fun out of chopping up his dad. Now he had to worry about getting overthrown while everyone else got to enjoy the good life. Uncool.

His relatives didn't visit him much anymore. Once Gaea went back into the earth, they stopped coming by the palace for Sunday dinner. They said they were busy, but Kronos suspected that his brothers, sisters, nieces, and nephews were simply scared of him. He *did* have his father's temper and sense of cruelty. His scythe was intimidating. Plus, he had the slightly off-putting tendency to scream, "I'll kill you all!" whenever someone made him mad. But was that *his* fault?

One morning he really snapped. He woke up to a Cyclops hammering on a piece of bronze right outside his bedroom window. Seven in the morning, on a *weekend*!

Kronos had promised his mom he would free the Elder Cyclopes and the Hundred-Handed Ones from Tartarus, but he was getting really tired of his ugly relatives. They'd become more and more disgusting as they grew up. They smelled like Porta Potties. They had, like, *zero* personal hygiene, and they were constantly making noise—building things, hammering metal, cutting stone. They'd been useful for building the palace, but now they were just annoying.

Kronos called Atlas and Hyperion and a couple of his other goons. They rounded up the Cyclopes and Hundred-Handed Ones and told them they were going for a nice drive in the country to look at wildflowers. Then they jumped the poor guys, wrapped them in chains again, and tossed them back into Tartarus.

If Gaea woke up, she wouldn't be happy—but so what? Kronos was the king now. Mom would just have to deal with it.

Things were much quieter at the palace after that, but Kronos still had a major case of the grumpies. It wasn't fair that he couldn't have a girlfriend.

In fact, he had a particular girl in mind.

Secretly, he had a crush on Rhea.

She was *gorgeous*. Every time the Titan family got together, Kronos stole glances at her. If he noticed any of the other guys flirting with her, he would pull them aside for a private conversation with his scythe in hand, and warn them never to do it again.

He loved how Rhea laughed. Her smile was brighter than Helios's chick magnet . . . uh, I mean the sun. He loved the way her dark curly hair swept her shoulders. Her eyes were as green as meadows, and her lips . . . well, Kronos dreamed about kissing those lips.

Also, Rhea was sweet and kind and everyone loved her. Kronos thought: If I just had a wife like that, my family wouldn't fear me as much. They'd come to the palace more often. Rhea would teach me to be a better Titan. Life would be awesome!

But another part of him thought, No! I can't get married, because of that stupid curse!

Kronos grumbled in frustration. He was the king of the freaking universe! He could do whatever he wanted! Maybe Ouranos had just been messing with him and there *was* no curse. Or maybe he would get lucky and he wouldn't have kids.

Note to self: If you're trying not to have kids, don't marry a lady who is the Titan of motherhood.

Kronos tried to restrain himself, but finally he couldn't stand it any longer. He invited Rhea to a romantic dinner and poured out his feelings. He proposed to her on the spot.

Now, I don't know if Rhea loved the guy or not. If she didn't, I imagine she was too afraid to say so. This was Kronos the Crooked One, after all—the dude who had killed their dad. The king of the freaking universe.

It didn't help that the whole time they ate dinner, his scythe was resting on a hook on the wall right behind him, its blade gleaming in the candlelight like it was still covered in golden ichor.

Rhea agreed to marry him.

Maybe she thought she could make him into a better guy. Maybe *Kronos* believed that, too. They had a nice honeymoon. A few weeks later, when Kronos heard that (surprise, surprise) Rhea was expecting their first child, he tried to convince himself everything was fine. He was happy! He would never be a bad father like Ouranos. It didn't matter if the baby was a boy Titan or a girl Titan. Kronos would love him or her and forget all about that old curse.

Then the kid was born—a beautiful baby girl.

Rhea had been secretly worried her child might turn out to be a Cyclops or a Hundred-Handed One. Maybe Kronos had been stressing about that, too. But nope. The child was perfect.

In fact, she was a little *too* perfect.

Rhea named her Hestia. She swaddled the baby in soft blankets and showed her to her proud papa. At first, Kronos smiled. The kid was not a monster—sweet! But as he tickled her chin and looked into her eyes and made the usual cute *goo-goo* noises, Kronos realized Hestia wasn't exactly a Titan.

She was smaller than a Titan baby, but heavier and perfectly proportioned. Her eyes were much too intelligent for a newborn. She radiated power. With Kronos's understanding of time, he could easily envision what this girl would look like when she grew up. She would be smaller than a Titan, but capable of great things. She would surpass any Titan at whatever she chose to do.

Hestia was like an improved version of the Titans—Titan

2.0, the Next Big Thing. In fact, she wasn't a Titan at all. She was a *goddess*—the first member of an entirely new branch of immortal evolution.

Looking at her, Kronos felt like an old cell phone staring at the latest model smartphone. He knew his days were numbered.

His proud papa smile faded. This kid could *not* be allowed to grow up, or the prophecy of Ouranos would come true. Kronos had to act fast. He knew Rhea would never agree to have her child killed, and she'd brought those stupid lions with her as usual. He couldn't have a fight in the throne room. Besides, he couldn't reach for his scythe while holding the baby. He had to get rid of Hestia immediately and irreversibly.

He opened his mouth—super, super wide, wider than he even realized he could. His lower jaw was hinged like on one of those massive snakes that can eat a cow. He stuffed Hestia in his mouth and swallowed her whole.

Just like: *GULP.* She was gone.

As you can imagine, Rhea completely freaked.

"My baby!" she screamed. "You—you just—"

"Oh, wow." Kronos belched. "My bad. Sorry."

Rhea's eyes bugged out. She screamed some more. She would have launched herself at Kronos and pummeled him with her fists, or ordered her lions to attack, but she was afraid of hurting the baby that was now stuck inside him.

"Cough her up!" Rhea demanded.

"Can't," Kronos said. "I have this super-strong stomach. Once something goes down, it doesn't come back up."

"How could you swallow her?" she shouted. "That was our child!"

"Yeah, about that . . ." Kronos tried to look apologetic. "Listen, babe, it wasn't going to work out with that kid."

"Work out?"

"There was this curse." Kronos told her what Ouranos had prophesied. "I mean, come on, sweetcakes! That baby wasn't even a proper Titan. She was trouble, I could tell! The next kid will be better, I'm sure."

This sounded perfectly reasonable to Kronos, but for some reason Rhea wasn't satisfied. She stormed off in a rage.

You'd think Rhea would never forgive him. I mean, your husband eats your firstborn child like a slider hamburger. . . . Your typical mother isn't going to forget that.

But Rhea's situation was complicated.

First, Kronos had swallowed the baby Hestia *whole*. Hestia, like her parents, was technically immortal. She couldn't die, even inside her father's stomach. Gross in there? Yes. A little claustrophobic? You bet. But fatal? No.

She's still alive, Rhea consoled herself. *I can find a way to get her back.*

That calmed her down a little, though she didn't have a plan. She couldn't use force to get her way. Rhea was a gentle goddess. Even if she tried to fight, most of the strongest Titans, like Hyperion and that big goon Atlas, would back Kronos up.

She couldn't risk a sneak attack with a knife or the scythe or even her lions, because that might hurt the baby.

Maybe you're thinking, *Wait a minute. If the kid is immortal, why is Rhea worried about hurting her?* But, see, immortals can be hurt badly, crippled, or mutilated. An injury might not kill them, but they also don't always *heal* from damage. They just stay crippled forever. You'll see some examples of that later on.

Rhea wasn't about to cut open Kronos and risk chopping up her baby, because being in pieces is no way to live, especially when you live forever.

She couldn't divorce Kronos, because nobody had invented divorce yet. And even if they had, Rhea would have been too scared to try. Can you blame her? As you may have noticed, Kronos was one crazy piece of work. Rhea had known that fact ever since he chopped up their dad with the scythe and then walked around the after-party in his ichor-stained shirt shouting, "Awesome murder, guys! High five!"

She couldn't run, because Kronos was lord of the whole world. Unless she wanted to jump into Tartarus (which she didn't), there was no place to go.

Her best bet was to stick it out, bide her time, and wait until she found a way to get Hestia back.

Kronos tried to be nice to her. He bought her presents and took her out to dinner, as if that could make her forget about the baby in his stomach.

When Kronos thought enough time had passed—like three or four days—he insisted that they try to have more kids.

Why? Maybe he had a secret death wish. Maybe he became obsessed with Ouranos's prophecy and wanted to see if the next kid would be a proper Titan or one of those horrible, too-powerful, too-perfect little *gods*.

So Rhea had another baby—a little girl even cuter than the first. Rhea named her Demeter.

Rhea dared to hope. Demeter was *so* adorable, maybe she would melt Kronos's heart. He couldn't possibly feel threatened by this little bundle of joy.

Kronos took the child in his arms and saw right away that Demeter was another goddess. She glowed with an aura even more powerful than Hestia's. She was trouble with a capital *tau*.

This time he didn't hesitate. He opened his jaws and swallowed her down.

Cue the screaming fit from Mom. Cue the apologies.

Rhea was *seriously* tempted to call out her lions, but now the stakes were even higher. Kronos had two kids in there.

I know, you're thinking it must've been getting crowded in the Titan lord's gut. But gods are kind of flexible about their size. Sometimes they are huge. Sometimes they're no bigger than humans.

I was not there in Kronos's stomach, thankfully, but I'm guessing the little immortal babies just made themselves small. They continued to mature, but they didn't get any bigger. They were like springs getting wound up tighter and tighter, hoping that someday they would get to burst out fully grown. And every day praying that Kronos wouldn't have hot sauce with his dinner.

Poor Rhea. Kronos insisted they try again.

"The next child will be better," he promised. "No more swallowing babies!"

The third kid? Also a girl. Rhea named her Hera, and she was the least Titan-ish, most godly yet. Rhea was indeed the Great Mother. In fact, she was a little *too* good at it. Every child she had was better and more powerful than the one before.

Rhea didn't want to take little Hera to Kronos, but it was a tradition back then. Dad got to hold the baby. It was one of those natural laws that Themis always insisted on. (There was also a natural law against eating your kids, but Themis was too afraid to mention that to Kronos.)

And so Rhea mustered her courage. "My lord, may I present your daughter Hera."

GULP.

This time, Rhea left the throne room without throwing a fit. She was too numb with pain and misery and disbelief. She had married a pathological liar who was also a murderer and a cannibal baby-eater.

Could things be any worse?

Oh, wait! He was also the king of the universe with lots of powerful henchmen, so she couldn't fight back or run away.

Yeah. Things were worse.

Two more times she gave birth to perfect, lovely god babies. The fourth child was a boy named Hades. Rhea hoped Kronos would let him live, because every dad wants a son to play catch with, right? Nope. Down the hatch, matey!

The fifth child was another boy, Poseidon. Same story. *SNARF.*

At this point, Rhea fled the palace. She wept and wailed and didn't know *what* to do. She went to her brothers and sisters, her nieces and nephews, anyone who would listen. She pleaded for help. The other Titans were either too scared of Kronos (like Themis), or they *worked* for Kronos (like Hyperion) and told her to stop whining.

Finally Rhea visited her sister Phoebe at the Oracle of Delphi, but sadly, even the Oracle had no advice for her. Rhea ran to the nearest meadow, threw herself on the ground, and began to cry. Suddenly she heard whispering from the earth. It was the voice of Gaea, who was still asleep; but even in her dreams the Earth Mother couldn't stand to hear the wailing of her lovely daughter.

When you are ready to deliver your next child, Gaea's voice whispered, *go to Crete to give birth! You will find help there! This child will be different! He will save the others!*

Rhea sniffled and tried to pull herself together. "Where is Crete?"

It's an island in the south, Gaea's voice said. *You take the Ionian Sea down to, like, Kalamata. Then you turn left and— You know what? You'll find it.*

When the time came and Rhea started to get very big in the belly, she took a few deep breaths, composed herself, and waddled into the throne room.

"My lord Kronos," she said, "I am off to Crete. I will be back with the baby."

"Crete?" Kronos scowled. "Why Crete?"

"Um, well," Rhea said, "you know how Koios and Phoebe sometimes have glimpses of the future?"

"Yeah?"

"I didn't want to spoil the surprise, but they prophesied that if I had this child in Crete, it would please you best of all! And of course, my lord, I am all about pleasing you!"

Kronos frowned. He was suspicious, but he also thought: Hey, I've eaten five kids, and Rhea is still here. If she were going to try something fishy, she would've done it already.

Plus, by now his thoughts were getting a little sluggish. He had five young gods shifting around in his gut, fighting for space, so he always felt like he'd just eaten a massive dinner and needed a nap.

I mean, five gods in one stomach—*dang.* That's enough for

doubles tennis, including a ref. They'd been down there so long, they were probably hoping Kronos would swallow a deck of cards or a Monopoly game.

Anyway, Kronos looked at Rhea and said, "You'll bring the baby to me immediately?"

"Of course."

"Okay. Off you go. Where is Crete?"

"Not sure," Rhea said. "I'll find it."

And she did. Once she got there, she was immediately met by some helpful nymphs who had also heard the voice of Gaea. They brought Rhea to a cozy, well-hidden cave at the base of Mount Ida. The nymphs' stream ran nearby, so Rhea would have lots of fresh water. The bountiful forest offered plenty to eat.

Yes, I know: immortals live mostly on nectar and ambrosia; but in a pinch they could eat other stuff. Being a god wouldn't be much fun if you couldn't enjoy the occasional pizza.

Rhea gave birth to a healthy baby boy god. He was the most beautiful and perfect one yet. Rhea named him Zeus, which, depending on who you ask, either means *Sky* or *Shining* or simply *Living*. I personally vote for the last one, because I think at this point Rhea had simple hopes for this kid—keep him alive and away from hostile stomachs.

Zeus began to cry, maybe because he sensed his mother's anxiety. The sound echoed through the cave and out into the world—so loud that everyone and their Titan mother knew a baby had been born.

"Oh, great," Rhea muttered. "I promised to bring the child to Kronos immediately. Now word will get back to Kronos that it's baby-swallowing time."

The cave floor rumbled. A large stone emerged from the dirt—a smooth, oval rock exactly the same size and weight as a baby god.

Rhea wasn't stupid. She knew this was a gift from Gaea. Normally, you would not be excited if your mom gave you a rock for a present, but Rhea understood what to do with it. She wrapped the stone in swaddling clothes and gave the real baby Zeus to the nymphs to take care of. She just hoped she could pull off the switcheroo once she got back to the palace.

"I'll visit as often as I can," Rhea promised the nymphs. "But how will you care for the baby?"

"Don't sweat it," said Neda, one of the nymphs. "We can feed him honey from the bees nearby. And for milk, we have an *awesome* immortal goat."

"A what, now?" Rhea asked.

The nymphs brought in their goat Amaltheia, who produced excellent magical goat milk in many different flavors, including low fat, chocolate, and baby formula.

"Nice goat," Rhea admitted. "But what if the baby cries? Kronos has incredible hearing up there on Mount Othrys. You may have noticed this kid has a set of lungs on him. Kronos will suspect something."

Neda considered this. She led Rhea to the cave entrance and called out to the Earth Mother: "Oh, Gaea! I know you're asleep, and all. Sorry to disturb you. But we could use some help guarding this kid! Preferably some very loud help!"

The ground rumbled again. Three new helpers emerged, born of dirt and the spilled blood of Ouranos (like I said, that stuff got *everywhere*). The new guys were large, hairy humanoids, dressed in fur and feathers and leather like they were on their way to some primeval festival deep in the rain forest. They were armed with spears and shields, so they looked more like head-hunters than nursemaids.

"WE ARE THE KOURETES!" one shouted at the top of his lungs. "WE WILL HELP!"

"Thank you," Rhea said. "Do you have to speak so loudly?"

"THIS IS MY INSIDE VOICE!" the warrior yelled.

Baby Zeus began crying again. The three warriors immediately busted out some sweet tribal dance moves, beating their spears on their shields and shouting and chanting. They covered up the crying just fine.

For some reason, Baby Zeus seemed to like the noise. He went to sleep in the nymph Neda's arms, and the Kouretes stopped.

"Okay, well," Rhea said, her ears popping, "looks like you have things under control here." She hefted her fake baby. "Wish me luck."

Once she got back to Mount Othrys, Rhea stormed into the throne room with her swaddled boulder. She was terrified her plan wouldn't work, but after so many years married to Kronos, she was learning to be a good actress. She marched right up to King Cannibal and shouted, "This is the best baby yet! A fine little boy named, uh, Rocky! And I suppose you're going to eat him!"

Kronos grimaced. Honestly, he wasn't excited about swallowing another baby god. He was full! But when you're king, you do what you have to do.

"Yeah—sorry, hon," he said. "I have to. Prophecy, and all."

"I hate you!" she screamed. "Ouranos was a horrible father, but at least he didn't swallow us!"

Kronos snarled. "Give me that child!"

"No!"

Kronos roared. He unhinged his jaw and showed his extreme mouth-opening skills. "NOW!"

He snatched up the swaddled boulder and stuffed it down his throat without even looking at it, just as Rhea had hoped.

In Kronos's belly, the five undigested young gods heard the rock rolling down the esophagus.

"Incoming!" yelled Poseidon.

They shifted—as much as they could in the cramped space—and Rocky landed in their midst.

"This is not a baby," Hades noticed. "I think it's a rock."

He was observant that way.

Meanwhile, in the throne room, Rhea threw an Oscar-worthy tantrum. She screamed and stomped her feet and called Kronos all kinds of unflattering names.

"RO-O-CCCKY!" she wailed. "NO-O-O-O-O-O!"

Kronos started to get a bad stomachache.

"That kid was *filling*," he complained. "What have you been feeding him?"

"Why should you care?" Rhea wailed. "I will never have another child again!"

That was okay with Kronos. He was stuffed.

Rhea ran screaming out of the throne room, and he didn't try to stop her.

Eventually, things quieted down in the palace. Kronos was now convinced he had thwarted the curse of Ouranos. No way could his children displace him, since he knew exactly where they all were. He was the king of the cosmos and would never be overthrown!

Meanwhile, Rhea visited Mount Ida whenever she could. Her baby boy began to grow up, and Rhea made sure he heard lots of bedtime stories about his horrible father and his five undigested siblings who were just waiting to be rescued from Kronos's gut.

So you *know* that when Zeus comes of age, there's going to be a father-son smackdown of epic proportions. If you want a "happily ever after" ending for Kronos and his Titans, I would stop reading now. Because in the next chapter, Zeus goes nuclear.

THE OLYMPIANS
BASH SOME HEADS

ZEUS HAD A GOOD CHILDHOOD ON MOUNT IDA. He spent his days romping around the countryside with nymphs and satyrs, learning to fight with his loud friends the Kouretes, eating his fill of honey and magical goat milk (yum!), and of course never going to school, because school hadn't been invented yet.

By the time he was a young adult god, he had grown into a good-looking dude—all tan and ripped from his time in the forest and at the beach. He had short black hair, a neatly trimmed beard, and eyes as blue as the sky, though they could cloud over *very* fast when he got angry.

One day his mom, Rhea, came to visit on her chariot pulled by lions.

"Zeus," she said, "you need a summer job."

Zeus scratched his beard. He liked the word *summer.* He

wasn't so sure about the word *job*. "What did you have in mind?"

Rhea's eyes gleamed. She had been planning her revenge on Kronos for a long time. Now, looking at her son—so confident, strong, and handsome—she knew the time had come.

"There's an opening at the palace for a cupbearer," she said.

"But I have no experience bearing cups," Zeus said.

"It's easy," Rhea promised. "Whenever King Kronos asks for a drink, you bring it to him. The pay isn't great, but the job has good side benefits, such as overthrowing your father and becoming lord of the cosmos."

"I'm down with that," Zeus said. "But won't Kronos recognize me as a god?"

"I've been thinking about that," Rhea said. "Your siblings have survived in Kronos's gut all these years and, like you, they're fully grown by now. That means they must have the power to change their size and shape. *You* should have that power, too. See if you can make yourself appear less godly, more . . . Titan-ish."

Zeus considered that. He had already discovered his ability to change shape. Once, he'd scared his caretaker nymphs by transforming into a bear. Another time he'd won a footrace with some satyrs by transforming into a wolf. The satyrs claimed he'd cheated, but he *totally* hadn't. It was a footrace. Wolves ran on their feet. It's not like he'd turned into an eagle (which he could also do).

The only Titan that Zeus had ever seen up close was his mother, but he knew Titans were generally bigger than he was. They didn't radiate power the way he did. They gave off a slightly different vibe—more violent and rougher around the edges. He imagined himself as a Titan. When he opened his eyes, he was taller than his mom for the first time. He felt as if he'd slept badly after a hard day strangling his enemies.

"Well done!" Rhea said. "Now, let's go to your job interview."

When Zeus saw Mount Othrys for the first time, his jaw dropped. The palace was *huge*. Its gleaming black towers rose into the clouds like greedy fingers grasping for the stars.

The fortress was meant to inspire fear. Zeus understood that immediately. But it also seemed lonely and dismal—not a fun place to be king. Zeus decided that if he ever got his own crib, it would be much cooler than Othrys. He wouldn't go so heavy on the whole "Lord of Darkness" look. His palace would be brilliant, blinding white.

One thing at a time, he told himself. *I have to bear cups first.*

Rhea escorted her son into the royal hall, where Old King Cannibal was snoozing on his throne. The years had not been kind to Kronos, which was ironic, since he was the lord of time. He hadn't *aged*, exactly, but he seemed tired and listless. Making mortal life forms wither and die no longer amused him. Stepping on humans didn't make him laugh like it used to, despite their cute little shrieks.

He'd put on weight from eating and drinking so much. The five gods in his stomach didn't help. They'd gotten bigger and heavier over the years. They were constantly trying to break out by climbing up Kronos's throat. Their attempts were unsuccessful, but they gave Kronos terrible acid reflux.

Rhea approached the throne. "My lord, I have someone for you to meet!"

Kronos snorted and opened his eyes. "I wasn't asleep!" He

blinked at the handsome young Titan who stood before him. "Who . . . ?"

The young immortal bowed low. "I am Zeus, my lord." Zeus had decided to use his real name, because—why not? Kronos had never heard it. "I would like to be your cupbearer."

Kronos studied the newcomer's face. Something about him seemed vaguely familiar—the sparkle in his eyes, the crooked way he smiled. Of course *all* the Titans were related. Maybe that was it. Kronos had so many nieces and nephews these days, he couldn't keep track of them all. Still, he found this young one unsettling. . . .

He looked around, trying to remember exactly who had introduced the boy, but Rhea had already faded into the shadows. Kronos's stomach was too full and his thoughts were too sluggish for him to stay suspicious for very long.

"Well," he said to the boy, "do you have any experience bearing cups?"

Zeus grinned. "No, my lord. But I'm a quick learner. I can also sing, dance, and tell satyr jokes."

Zeus burst into a song the nymphs had taught him. Then he demonstrated some Kouretes dance moves. It was the most interesting thing that had happened on Mount Othrys in a long time. Other Titans gathered in the throne room to watch. Soon they were cheering and laughing. Even Kronos had a smile on his face.

"You're hired," Kronos said. "In fact, I'm thirsty."

"One cup, coming up!" Zeus hustled off to find the kitchen, where he filled a golden chalice with ice-cold nectar.

In no time, Zeus became the most popular servant in the palace. He bore cups like nobody's business. His singing was as clear as the streams on Mount Ida. His satyr jokes were so edgy, I can't tell them in a family-friendly book.

He always knew exactly what Kronos would like to drink—hot spiced nectar, cold nectar with a twist of lemon, nectar spritzer with a little cranberry juice. He also introduced the Titans to drinking contests, which were very popular with the satyrs back on Mount Ida. Everybody at the table started chugging at the same time. The fastest drinker won. What did he win? Well, nothing—but it was a great way to show off, because nothing looks more manly (or Titanly) than having nectar dribbling down your chin and all over your shirt.

These contests rekindled some of Kronos's competitive spirit. Sure, he was king of the universe, but he was still the youngest of twelve kids. He couldn't allow his brothers or nephews to be better than him at anything. Despite his constantly full stomach, he got to the point where he could chug a full goblet of nectar in three seconds, and Titan goblets are the size of water cooler jugs.

He trusted Zeus to fill his glass with whatever would go down the smoothest.

Which was exactly Zeus's plan.

One night when Kronos was dining with his favorite lieutenants, Zeus mixed some special brews for the drinking contest. The nymphs back on Mount Ida had taught him a lot about herbs and stuff. He knew which plants could make you drowsy, which ones could make you dizzy, and which could make you feel so *terrible,* your stomach would want to exit your body.

For the king's guests, Zeus mixed some sleepy-time extra-dizzy nighty-night nectar. For Kronos, he mixed a special blend of nectar and mustard. Some versions of the story will say Zeus used wine, but that can't be right, because wine hadn't been invented yet. We'll get to that later.

Anyway, the stuff in Kronos's goblet was über-nasty. Zeus set it aside and waited for the right moment.

Dinner started out as usual, with lots of drinking, eating, and catching up on the Titan news of the day. Zeus kept the nectar flowing. He entertained the guests with his jokes and his singing. Toward the end of the evening, when everybody was content and relaxed and sleepy, Zeus began boasting about the king's drinking skill.

"Kronos is the boss at drinking!" he proclaimed. "You should *see* him. The guy is *insane.* I mean his record is, what—three seconds?"

"Urg," Kronos said. He was full already and had been hoping to avoid a drinking contest.

"If he wanted to," Zeus said, "he could drink faster than all of you! I bet he would set a new world record tonight. Wouldn't you love to see that?"

Atlas, Hyperion, Koios, and the others cheered and called for a contest.

Kronos *really* wasn't in the mood, but he couldn't decline. His honor as a super-chugger was at stake. He gestured for Zeus to bring in another round.

Zeus ran to the kitchen and fetched his special concoctions. He offered the guests their sleepy-time nectar, then served Kronos last, giving the king no time to smell his brew before yelling, "Ready, set, go!"

The Titans gulped down their tasty beverages. Kronos

immediately noticed that his nectar tasted weird, but it was a contest. He couldn't stop chugging. The whole point was to drain the cup! Maybe his taste buds were just a little off. After all, Zeus had never steered him wrong.

Kronos drained his nectar in two and a half seconds. He slammed the goblet upside down on the table and shouted: "I win! I—"

The next sound out of his mouth was like a walrus getting the Heimlich maneuver.

There's no pleasant way to say it. Kronos puked. He puked a puke worthy of the king of the universe. It was a *kingly* puke.

His stomach tried to propel itself out his throat. His mouth hinged open all by itself—the better to upchuck you with, my dear—and shot out five gods, a very slimy rock, quite a lot of nectar, some biscuits, and a chariot license plate. (No, I don't know how *that* got in there.)

The five disgorged gods immediately grew to full-size adults right there on the dining table. The Titan guests stared in amazement, their minds working slowly due to the spiked nectar.

As for Kronos, he was still trying to catapult his guts across the throne room.

"Get—" He retched. "—them!"

Atlas was the first to react. He yelled, "Guards!" and tried to stand, but he was so dizzy, he fell right into Hyperion's lap.

Zeus wanted to lunge for his father's scythe. He wanted to slice up the old cannibal on the spot, but the other Titans were starting to recover from their shock. They might be slow and sleepy, but they had weapons. Meanwhile, Zeus's only weapon was a serving tray. His army consisted of five slimy, unarmed gods who had spent very little time outside a stomach, much less in combat.

Guards started pouring into the throne room.

Zeus turned to his confused siblings. "I'm your brother Zeus. Follow me, and I will give you freedom and revenge. Also honey and goat milk."

That was good enough for the gods. While Kronos retched and his fighters fumbled with their weapons, Zeus and his siblings turned into eagles and soared out of the palace.

"Now what?" Hades asked.

The six gods had gathered at Zeus's secret lair on Mount Ida, which his siblings refused to call the Zeus Cave. Zeus had briefed them on what was happening in the world, but they all knew they couldn't stay on Mount Ida very long. The nymphs had heard rumors whispered through the earth: Kronos was sending his Titans to scour the world for the escapees. He wanted them brought back, either in chains or in small pieces. He wasn't particular.

"Now we fight," Zeus said.

Poseidon grunted. He'd only been out of Kronos's gut for a day, but he was already starting to dislike his youngest brother—this upstart *Zeus*, who thought he should be in charge just because he had rescued them.

"I'm all for fighting Dad," Poseidon said, "but that requires weapons. Do you have any?"

Zeus scratched his ear. He hadn't really thought that far ahead. "Well, no. . . ."

"Perhaps we can make peace," Hestia suggested.

The others stared at her as if she were crazy. Hestia was the eldest and gentlest of the gods, but her siblings didn't take her seriously. You have to wonder how the world might've been different if Hestia had been put in charge, but alas, she wasn't.

"Uh, no," said Demeter. "I will never forgive our father. Perhaps we could steal his scythe. We could chop him up like he did Ouranos! Then I could use the scythe for something better—like cutting wheat! Did you see those beautiful fields we flew over?"

Hera scowled at her sister. "What is it with you and crops? All those years in Kronos's gut, all you ever talked about was plants, which you never even saw before today!"

Demeter blushed. "I don't know. I always dream about green fields. They're so peaceful and beautiful and—"

"My children!" said a voice from the woods.

Mother Rhea stepped into the clearing. She hugged each of her precious sons and daughters, weeping tears of joy over their freedom. Then she drew them together and said, "I know where you can get weapons."

She told them the story of the Hundred-Handed Ones and the Elder Cyclopes, whom Kronos had exiled to Tartarus for a second time.

"The Hundred-Handed Ones are incredible stonemasons," Rhea said. "They built Kronos's palace."

"Which is pretty awesome," Zeus admitted.

"They are strong, and they hate Kronos," Rhea continued. "They would be good in battle. As for the Cyclopes, they are talented blacksmiths. If anyone can forge weapons more powerful than your father's scythe, they can."

Hades's dark eyes gleamed. The idea of descending into

the most dangerous, vilest part of creation somehow appealed to him. "So we go to Tartarus, and we bring back the Cyclopes and Hundred-Handed Ones."

"Piece of cake," said Hera. She knew about cake, because Kronos had eaten lots of it. The crumbs and icing were always getting in her hair. "Let's go."

A Tartarus jailbreak may not sound like an easy thing for you or me, but six gods can accomplish a lot when they put their minds to it. Hades found a cave system that led deep into the Underworld. He seemed to have a knack for navigating the tunnels. He led his siblings along the course of a subterranean river called the Styx until it spilled over a cliff into the void of Tartarus. The gods became bats (you could argue that they were already bats, but you know what I mean) and flew into the abyss.

At the bottom, they found a gloomy landscape of rock spires, gray wastes, fiery pits, and poisonous fog, with all sorts of nasty monsters and evil spirits roaming about. Apparently Tartarus, the spirit of the pit, had been breeding more primordial gods down there in the darkness, and they'd been having kids of their own.

The six young gods crept around until they found the maximum-security zone, surrounded by a high brass wall and patrolled by demons. In bat form the gods could fly over the wall easily; but once inside, they spotted the jailer and almost lost their nerve.

Kronos had personally hired the most horrible monster in Tartarus to make sure his high-value prisoners never escaped.

Her name was Kampê.

I don't know if Kronos found her on Craigslist or what, but if the worst creatures from your nightmares had nightmares of their own, they would probably dream about Kampê. From the waist up, she was a humanoid female with snakes for hair. (If that sounds familiar, it's because the hairdo really caught on with other monsters later.) From the waist down, she was a four-legged dragon. Thousands of vipers sprouted from her legs like grass skirts. Her waist was ringed with the heads of fifty hideous beasts—bears, boars, wombats, you name it— always snapping and snarling and trying to eat Kampê's shirt.

Large, dark reptilian wings grew from her shoulder blades. Her scorpionlike tail swished back and forth, dripping venom. Basically, Kampê didn't get invited on many dates.

The gods watched from behind a pile of boulders as the monstrous jailer tromped back and forth, lashing the Elder Cyclopes with a fiery whip and stinging the Hundred-Handed Ones with her scorpion tail whenever they got out of line.

The poor prisoners were forced to work without any break—no water, no sleep, no food, nothing. The Hundred-Handed Ones spent their time at the far end of the yard, quarrying stone blocks from the hard volcanic floor. The Cyclopes worked at the closer end. They each had a forge where they smelted metals and hammered out sheets of bronze and iron. If the Cyclopes tried to sit down, or even pause long enough to catch their breaths, Kampê would leave fresh burning lash marks across their backs.

Even worse, the prisoners weren't allowed to finish anything they started. As soon as the Hundred-Handed Ones had a goodly stack of building blocks, Kampê forced them to break their quarried stone into rubble. Whenever the Cyclopes were on the verge of finishing a weapon or a shield or even a tool that might be dangerous, Kampê confiscated it and threw it into the bubbling pits of magma.

You're probably thinking: *Hey, there were six big dudes and only one Kampê. Why didn't they overpower her?*

But Kampê had the whip. The venom in her tail could incapacitate even an Elder Cyclops for hours, leaving him writhing in pain. The dragon lady was straight-up *terrifying*, and the prisoners were chained around their feet so they couldn't run far.

Besides, the Hundred-Handed Ones and the Cyclopes were gentle souls. Despite their looks, they were builders, not fighters. Give these dudes a bucket of Legos, and they'd be happy for days.

Zeus waited until Kampê marched to the far end of the prison yard. Then he sneaked up to the nearest Cyclops.

"Psst!" he called.

The Cyclops lowered his hammer. He turned toward Zeus, but his one big eye had been staring into the flames so long, he couldn't see who was talking.

"I am not Psst," the Cyclops said. "I am Brontes."

Oh, boy, Zeus thought. This may take a while.

"Hey, Brontes." Zeus spoke slowly and cheerfully, like he was trying to coax a puppy out of its box. "I'm Zeus. I've come to rescue you."

Brontes scowled. "I have heard that before. Kronos tricked us."

"Yeah, I know," Zeus said. "Kronos is my enemy too. Together, we can get revenge and throw *him* down here. How does that sound?"

"Sounds good," Brontes said. "But how?"

"First we need weapons," Zeus said. "Can you make us some?"

Brontes shook his head. "Kampê is always watching. She will not let us finish any project."

"How about you each make a different part of each weapon?" Zeus suggested. "Then you can assemble them at the last second and toss them over to us. Kampê will never know."

"You are smart."

"I know, right? Spread the word to your friends." Zeus crept back behind the boulders.

Brontes whispered the plan to his brothers Arges and Steropes. Then they tapped their hammers on their anvils in a secret code they'd developed, sending the message across the yard to the Hundred-Handed Ones—Briares, Kottos, and Gyes.

I know that's a bunch of horrible names, but remember, Gaea didn't have much time to hold her monstrous triplets before Ouranos pitched them into Tartarus. At least they didn't end up named Huey, Dewey, and Louie.

The gods waited in the darkness while the Cyclopes forged pieces of the new weapons, making each one look like a harmless, incomplete doohickey. I don't know if the stuff would've gotten through airport security, but it was good enough to fool Kampê.

The next time the she-dragon turned her back and marched toward the far side of the yard, Brontes quickly assembled the first magic weapon and tossed it to Zeus. It looked like a bronze rocket, about four feet long, with nose cones on both ends. Zeus's hand fit perfectly around the center. As soon as he lifted it, his whole body tingled with power.

Poseidon frowned. "What *is* that? It's not a scythe."

Sparks flew from the points. Electricity arced from one end to the other. Zeus aimed the thing at a nearby boulder, and a thousand tendrils of lightning zapped it into dust.

"Oh, yeah," Zeus said. "I can work with this."

Fortunately, Kampê didn't seem to notice the blast. Maybe things exploded a lot in Tartarus.

A few minutes later, Brontes tossed them a second weapon—a spear with three prongs. Poseidon caught it.

He immediately fell in love with the trident. He liked pointy things! Also, he could feel the power of storms humming through the spear. When he concentrated, a miniature tornado swirled around its three points, getting faster and larger the more he focused. When he planted the spear on the ground, the floor of the pit began to shake and crack.

"Best weapon," he announced. "Right here."

Brontes tossed them a third item. Hades caught this one—a gleaming bronze war helmet decorated with scenes of death and destruction.

"You get weapons," Hades grumbled. "I get a hat."

He put it on and disappeared.

"Dude, you're invisible," Zeus said.

"Yeah." Hades sighed miserably. "I'm used to it."

"No, I mean you're *actually* invisible."

"Huh." Hades willed himself to turn visible again.

"That is one scary hat," Demeter said.

"Yeah," Hades agreed. "Yeah, it is."

He decided to try something else. He glared at his brothers, and waves of terror radiated from the helmet. Zeus and

Poseidon turned pale. They started to sweat. Zeus almost dropped his new lightning maker.

"Stop that!" Zeus hissed. "You're freaking me out!"

Hades grinned. "Okay, maybe the hat isn't so bad."

Hera crossed her arms and sniffed disdainfully. "Boys and their toys. I don't suppose *we* get weapons? Are we just supposed to stand back and be cheerleaders while you three do the fighting?"

Zeus winked at her. "Don't worry, baby. I'll protect you."

"I think I'm going to be sick," Hera said.

It's possible the Cyclopes would have made weapons for the women. But at that moment Kampê turned and marched back toward the Cyclopes. Maybe she had noticed the smoke from Zeus's lightning blast, or the swirling clouds from Poseidon's trident. Maybe she could taste the residual fear in the air from Hades's helmet. Whatever tipped her off, she detected the presence of the gods.

She raised her whip and howled, "RAWRGGGGWRRR!"

She charged toward their hiding place, her tail lashing, the thousands of vipers around her legs dripping poison.

"Great," muttered Hera.

"I got this," Zeus promised.

He stood and raised his bronze lightning bolt. He focused all his energy into the weapon.

KA-BLAM!

A column of white-hot power shot toward Kampê—the most blinding light that had ever been seen in Tartarus.

Kampê just had time to think *Uh-oh,* before the bolt blasted her into a million sizzling pieces of reptile confetti.

"THAT'S what I'm talking about!" Zeus yelled happily.

Poseidon lowered his trident. "Man, give the rest of us a chance."

"You go free the Cyclopes and the Hundred-Handed Ones," Zeus suggested.

Poseidon grumbled, but he used his trident to strike the dark chains from the prisoners' feet.

"Thank you," Brontes said. "We will help you fight Kronos."

"Excellent!" Zeus said.

Hera cleared her throat. "Yes, but about those weapons for the ladies—"

Outside the bronze walls, monstrous roars reverberated through the pit. Every spirit and beast in Tartarus had probably seen the flash of lightning, and now they were closing in to investigate.

"We should leave," Demeter said. "Like, right now."

That was the best non-grain-related idea Demeter had ever had, so Hades led his siblings back to the upper world, along with their six large new friends.

Kronos wasn't an easy guy to defeat.

By most accounts, the Titan War took ten years—or maybe Kronos just used his time tricks to make it *seem* that long, hoping the gods would give up. If so, it didn't work.

Rhea the Great Mother visited every Titan she could, trying to persuade them to side with Zeus. Many listened. After all, Kronos wasn't the most popular leader. Almost all the female Titans either helped Zeus or stayed out of his way. Prometheus, the creator of humans, was smart enough to remain neutral. Oceanus kept to himself in the depths of the ocean. Helios and Selene, the sun and moon, agreed not to take sides as long as they got to keep their jobs.

That left Kronos and most of the other male Titans, with Atlas as his general and champion fighter.

The gods and Titans skirmished back and forth—blowing up an island here, vaporizing a sea there. The Titans were strong and well armed. At the beginning, they held the advantage. Even with magic Cyclops weapons, the gods weren't used to combat. It's a hard thing not to drop your trident and run when Atlas is barreling down on you, screaming and waving his sword.

But the gods *did* learn to fight. The Cyclopes eventually armed all Zeus's allies with top-of-the-line weapons. The Hundred-Handed Ones learned to throw barrages of stones like living catapults.

You're thinking, *How hard can it be to throw rocks?*

Okay, *you* try throwing rocks with both hands at the same time and hitting your target. It's not as easy as it sounds. Now, imagine coordinating one hundred hands—all throwing rocks the size of refrigerators. If you're not careful, you'll spew rocks everywhere and crush yourself and your allies.

Once the gods learned to fight, the war *still* took a long time, because none of the combatants on either side could die. You couldn't just stab a guy, zap him, or throw a house on him and call it a day. You had to actually capture each enemy and make sure he was hurt so badly, he would never heal. Then you had to figure out what to do with his crippled body. As Zeus knew, even throwing somebody into Tartarus wasn't a guarantee he would stay gone forever.

Little skirmishes weren't going to decide anything.

Finally Zeus came up with his big plan.

"We have to storm Mount Othrys," he told his siblings at their weekly war meeting. "A full frontal assault on their head-quarters. If we do that, the hostile Titans will rally to protect Kronos. Then we can take them all down at once."

"In other words," Hades said, "you want us to commit *suicide*."

Poseidon leaned on his trident. "For once, I agree with Hades. If we march up the slopes of Mount Othrys, Atlas will be ready for us. His troops will have the high ground. They'll smash us flat. If we try flying in, we'll get shot out of the air. They've got plenty of anti-god missile weapons."

Zeus's eyes gleamed. "But I've got a different plan. We'll soften them up by attacking from the next mountain over."

"Do what, now?" asked Demeter. She looked uncomfort-able in her armor, even though she'd designed it herself. She'd painted a sheaf of barley and a daisy on her shield, and for her main weapon she'd chosen a fearsome garden trowel.

Zeus drew a map of the Greek mainland in the dirt. Near Mount Othrys was another Greek mountain—not quite as tall, not as well known. It was called Mount Olympus.

"We scale Olympus," Zeus said. "They won't be expecting that, but Othrys will be within range of our missile weapons. The Hundred-Handed Ones will launch volleys of boulders. I'll bust out the lightning. Poseidon will summon storms and earthquakes."

"And I'll turn invisible," Hades muttered.

Zeus clapped his brother on the shoulder. "You have an important job too. You send waves of terror through the enemy ranks. Once we've destroyed their defenses, we all fly over there—"

"Including us three goddesses?" Demeter prompted. "We can fight too, you know."

"Sure!" Zeus smiled nervously. "Did you think I'd forgotten you?"

"Yes," said Demeter.

"Uh, anyway," Zeus continued, "we fly over to Mount Othrys, smash anybody who's left standing, and take them all prisoner."

Hestia wrapped herself in her plain brown shawl. "I still think we should make peace."

"NO!" the others yelled.

Hera tapped the dirt map. "It's a crazy plan. I like it."

So that night, under cover of darkness, the gods and their allies climbed Mount Olympus for the first time.

The next morning, as Helios rode his chick magnet into the sky, King Kronos awoke to a sound like thunder. Probably because it *was* thunder.

Storm clouds rolled in from every direction. Zeus hurled a lightning bolt that blasted the tallest tower into black marble shrapnel. The Hundred-Handed Ones chucked so many boulders toward Mount Othrys that when Kronos looked out his window, it seemed to be raining major appliances.

The beautiful palace domes imploded in mushroom clouds of dust. Walls crumbled. Columns fell like dominoes. The Hundred-Handed Ones had built Mount Othrys, and they knew exactly how to destroy it.

As the palace shook, Kronos grabbed his scythe and called

his brethren to attack. But the thing was a) scythes really don't do much against boulders and lightning, b) nobody could hear him over the noise, and c) the palace was disintegrating around him. Just as he was saying, "Titans, let's go!" a three-ton section of the ceiling collapsed on his head.

The battle was a massacre, if you can have a massacre where nobody dies.

A few Titans tried to counterattack, only to be buried in an avalanche of rubble and boulders.

After the initial assault, the gods flew over and mopped up the resistance. Poseidon summoned earthquakes to swallow their enemies. Hades popped up in random places and yelled, "Boo!" His helmet of terror (or his Boo Cap, as the others called it) sent Titans fleeing straight off the sides of cliffs, or into the waiting arms of the Elder Cyclopes.

When the dust settled and the storm clouds lifted, even the gods were in awe of what they'd done.

Not only was Kronos's palace gone, but the entire top of Mount Othrys had been sheared away with it.

Did I tell you Othrys was the highest mountain in Greece? Not anymore. Today Mount Olympus, which *used* to be the smaller mountain, is over nine thousand feet tall. Mount Othrys is only five thousand and change. Zeus and the Hundred-Handed Ones had basically cut the mountain in half.

The Cyclopes dug the Titans out of the rubble and began chaining them up. None of them got away. General Atlas and the four brothers who controlled the corners of the earth were dragged before Zeus and made to kneel.

"Ah, my dear uncles!" Zeus chuckled. "Koios, Krios,

Hyperion, Iapetus—you four are going straight to Tartarus, where you will remain for all time!"

The four brothers hung their heads in shame, but General Atlas laughed at his captors.

"Puny gods!" he bellowed. Even wrapped in chains, he was intimidating. "You know nothing of how the universe works. If you throw these four into Tartarus, the entire sky will fall! Only their presence at the four corners of the earth keeps the wide expanse of Ouranos from crashing down upon us."

"Maybe." Zeus grinned. "But fortunately, Atlas, I have a solution! You're always boasting how strong you are. From now on, you're going to hold the sky up all by yourself!"

"What?"

"Brontes, Arges, Steropes," Zeus called. "He's all yours."

The Elder Cyclopes dragged Atlas to a distant mountaintop where the sky was very close. I don't know how they did it, but they caused the sky to form a new central support pillar—a single funnel cloud, like the bottom point of a spinning top. They chained Atlas to the mountain and forced the entire weight of the sky onto his shoulders.

Now you're thinking, *Why didn't he just refuse to hold it, and let the sky fall?*

I did mention the chains, right? He couldn't run away without getting flattened. Also, it's hard to appreciate unless you've done it (which I have), but holding the sky is kind of like being stuck under a loaded barbell during a bench press. All your concentration goes into keeping that thing from crushing you. You can't lift it, because it's too heavy. You can't release it, because it will squash you as it drops. All you can do is hold it in place, sweating and straining and whimpering "Help!" hoping somebody will walk through the gym, notice you being slowly pressed into a pancake, and lift the weight off you. But what if no one does? Imagine being stuck in that situation for *eternity*.

That was Atlas's punishment. All the other Titans who fought in the war got off easy. They were pitched headfirst into Tartarus.

Which leaves us with the million-drachma question: What happened to Kronos?

There are a lot of different stories. Most agree that the Crooked One was dug out of the rubble and brought before Zeus. Most say he was bound in chains like the other Titans and tossed into Tartarus.

According to some later traditions—and I kind of like this version—Zeus took his father's scythe and sliced him up the way Kronos had sliced up Ouranos. Kronos was thrown into Tartarus in teeny-tiny pieces. Supposedly, that's where we get the idea of Father Time with his scythe, being deposed every January first by Baby New Year—though it's difficult to imagine Zeus in a diaper and a party hat.

Some versions claim that Zeus released Kronos from Tartarus many years later—either to live out his retirement in Italy, or to rule the Isles of the Blest in Elysium. Personally, I don't buy that. It doesn't make sense if you believe that Kronos was chopped to bits. And if you know Zeus, you know he's not exactly the forgive-and-forget type.

Anyway, Kronos was done. The age of the Titans was over.

The Titans who *didn't* fight against the gods were allowed to stick around. Some, like Helios and Selene, kept their jobs. Some even intermarried with the gods.

Zeus named himself the new king of the cosmos, but he was smarter than Kronos. He sat down with his brothers and said, "Look, I want to be fair about this. How about we throw dice for control of different parts of the world? Highest roll gets first choice."

Hades frowned. "I have rotten luck. What parts are we talking about?"

"The sky, the sea, and the Underworld," Zeus offered.

"You mean Tartarus?" Poseidon asked. "Gross!"

"I mean the *upper* Underworld," Zeus said. "You know, the *nice* part nearer to the surface. That's not so bad—big caves, lots of jewels, riverside real estate on the Styx."

"Huh," Hades said. "What about the earth itself? Greece and all the other lands?"

"That will be neutral territory," Zeus suggested. "We can all operate on the earth."

The brothers agreed. Notice how the sisters were not invited to this little dice game? I know. Totally unfair. But that's how it went down.

No surprise, Zeus got the highest roll. He chose the sky for his domain, which made sense because of the lightning bolts, and all. Poseidon got the second-highest roll. He chose the sea and became the supreme god of the waters, above Oceanus, who got pushed ever farther to the margins of the world, and Pontus, who was mostly asleep in the muck all the time anyway.

Hades got the worst roll, as he expected. He took the Underworld as his domain, but it kind of suited his gloomy personality, so he didn't complain (much).

The Hundred-Handed Ones built Zeus the gleaming palace he'd always dreamed of at the top of Mount Olympus.

Then Zeus sent them back to Tartarus—but this time as jailers to watch over the Titans. The Hundred-Handed Ones didn't really mind. At least now *they* were the ones with the whips.

The Elder Cyclopes went to work for the gods. They constructed a workshop at the bottom of the sea near the island of Lemnos, where there was lots of volcanic heat to power their forges. They made tons of special weapons and other fun collectibles, and had a good health package with a week of paid vacation every year.

As for the gods, Zeus invited them all to live with him on Mount Olympus. Each of them had a throne in the main hall, so even though Zeus was in charge, it was more like a council than a dictatorship. They called themselves the Olympians.

Well . . . I *say* they were all welcome in Olympus: but Hades, not so much. The guy had always creeped out his siblings. Now that he was lord of the Underworld, he seemed to bring doom and darkness with him wherever he went.

"You understand," Zeus told him privately, "we can't have an Underworld throne up here on Mount Olympus. It would make the other gods uncomfortable, and the skulls and black stone really wouldn't go with the decor."

"Oh, sure," grumbled Hades. "I see how it is."

Anyway, that's how things got started with the gods on Mount Olympus. Eventually there would be twelve thrones in the council chamber, and a whole bunch of other gods who *didn't* have thrones.

The Olympians figured that now they could settle down and rule the world in peace.

There was only one problem. Remember that the Earth Mother Gaea was taking a nap all this time? Well, eventually she would wake up. And when she got home and found out her favorite kids, the Titans, had been thrown into Tartarus, Zeusie was going to have some explaining to do.

But that's a tale for another day.

Now it's time to meet the gods, up close and personal. Just be warned, some of their stories might make you feel like Kronos after a big glass of mustard nectar.

~~ZEUS~~

WHY IS ZEUS ALWAYS FIRST?

Seriously, every book about the Greek gods has to start with this guy. Are we doing reverse alphabetical order? I know he's the king of Olympus and all—but trust me, this dude's ego does *not* need to get any bigger.

You know what? Forget him.

We're going to talk about the gods in the order they were born, women first. Take a backseat, Zeus. We're starting with Hestia.

HESTIA CHOOSES BACHELOR NUMBER ZERO

I N SOME WAYS, Hestia was a lot like her mom, Rhea.

She had an honest smile, warm brown eyes, and black hair that framed her face in ringlets. She was gentle and good-natured. She never said a bad word about anybody. If you walked into a party on Mount Olympus, Hestia wouldn't be the first girl who caught your eye. She wasn't flashy or loud or crazy. She was more like the goddess next door—sweet and pretty in an unpretentious way. Usually she kept her hair tucked under a linen shawl. She wore plain, modest dresses and never used makeup.

I said earlier that nobody took her seriously, and it's true the other gods weren't good about taking her advice. Kronos had swallowed Hestia first, so she'd gotten barfed up last. Because of that, her siblings tended to think of her as the youngest rather than the oldest—the last one to emerge. She was quieter and more peaceful than her siblings, but that didn't mean they didn't *love* her. Like Rhea, Hestia was a hard person not to love.

In one important way, though, Hestia was *not* like Rhea. Her mom was known for being . . . well, a mom. The Great Mother. The Ultimate Mama. *La Madre Grande.*

Hestia wanted nothing to do with being a mom.

She didn't have a problem with *other* people's families. She loved her siblings, and once they started having kids, she loved them, too. Her fondest wish was for the whole Olympian family to get along and spend quality time together around the hearth, chatting or having dinner or playing Twister—really any wholesome activity.

Hestia just didn't want to get married herself.

If you think about it, you can see why. Hestia had spent years inside Kronos's gut. She had a very good memory, and could even recall Kronos gulping her down when she was a newborn. She remembered the sound of her mother wailing in despair. Hestia had nightmares that the same thing might happen to her. She didn't want to get married only to find out her husband was actually a baby-swallowing cannibal.

She wasn't being paranoid, either. She had *proof* that Zeus could be as bad as Kronos.

See, after the war with Kronos, Zeus decided it would be a good idea for him to marry a Titan, sort of to show there were no hard feelings. He married one of Oceanus's daughters, a girl named Metis, who was the Titan of good advice and planning—kind of like the Titans' life coach.

Metis was smart about advising others, but apparently she wasn't so bright when it came to her own life. When she was pregnant with her first kid, she told Zeus, "My husband, I have good news! I foresee that this child will be a girl. But if we have another child together, it will be a boy. And—you're going to love this—he will be destined to rule the universe some day! Isn't that awesome?"

Zeus panicked. He thought he was going to end up like Ouranos and Kronos—chopped into little pieces—so he took a page out of Kronos's playbook. He opened his mouth super-wide and created a tornado that sucked Metis right down his throat, compressing her so small that he could swallow her whole.

That kind of freaked out the other Olympians, especially Hestia.

What happened to Metis and her unborn child down there in Zeus's gut? We'll get to that later. But Hestia saw the whole thing, and she said to herself: *Getting married is DANGEROUS!*

Zeus apologized to the Titans and the gods for swallowing Metis. He promised never to do it again. He decided to marry another Titan, but as you can guess, there weren't a lot of vol-unteers. Only one agreed: Themis, the Titan of divine law, who happened to be Hestia's favorite aunt.

Themis had sided with the gods in the war. She under-stood right and wrong, and she knew that the gods would be better rulers than Kronos. (Notice I said *better*, not *good*.)

Like Hestia, Themis was modest and veiled and wasn't interested in marriage, especially after what happened to Metis; but in the name of peace, she agreed to marry Zeus.

(And yeah, Themis was technically Zeus's aunt, so feel free to get sick about them getting married. But let's move past that.)

The marriage didn't last long. Themis had two sets of trip-lets. The first set wasn't so bad—three sisters called the Horai, who ended up being in charge of the changing seasons.

(You're thinking, *Wait, only three seasons?* But remember, this was Greece. I guess they've never had much of a winter.)

The second set of triplets, though—they gave everyone the creeps. They were called the Morai, the Three Fates, and they were *born* old. Right out of the cradle, they grew from three shriveled babies into three shriveled old grannies. They liked to sit in the corner and make thread on a magic spinning wheel. Each time they snipped a piece of the line, some mortal down in the world died.

The Olympians quickly realized that the three Fates could not only see the future, they could *control* it. They could bind anyone's life to their magical yarn—literally making a lifeline— and when they snipped off that piece? Sayonara! Nobody was sure if they could do the same thing with immortals. But even Zeus was afraid of those girls.

After fathering the Fates, Zeus pulled Themis aside and said, "You know what? I'm not sure this marriage is going to work out. If we keep having more kids like those Fates, we're all going to be in trouble. What's next—the Three Doomsday Bombs? The Three Little Pigs?"

Themis pretended to be disappointed, but actually she was relieved. She didn't want any more kids, and she definitely didn't want to get sucked down the tornado of Zeus's throat.

"You're right, my lord," she said. "I will gladly step aside and let you take another wife."

Hestia witnessed all this, and she was thinking: I never want that to happen to me. With my luck, I would marry some god and give birth to the Three Stooges. No, the possibility is too horrible.

She decided it was much better to stay single and concentrate on helping her siblings raise *their* families. She could be the cool aunt. The single aunt. The aunt who did not have terrifying shriveled granny babies.

There was only one problem: some of the guy gods had other ideas. Poseidon kept looking at Hestia and thinking, Hey, she's kind of pretty. Good personality. Easy to get along with. I should marry her.

Yeah, we're back to the whole brother-marrying-sister thing. Let's get it out of our systems—all together, One, two, three: "GROSS!"

A younger Olympian, Apollo, also wanted to marry Hestia. We'll talk more about him later, but it would've been a weird match, since Apollo was one of the flashiest gods. Why he wanted to marry quiet, plainspoken Hestia, I don't know. Maybe he wanted a wife who would never upstage him.

As it happened, both gods approached Zeus on the same day, asking his permission to marry Hestia. Seems weird that they would ask *Zeus* instead of Hestia but, as you might have noticed, the males weren't real sensitive about stuff like that. Zeus, being the king of the cosmos, had the final say on all marriages.

Meanwhile, Hestia was sitting at the big hearth in the middle of the throne room, not paying much attention. Back then you needed a central hearth, like an open fire pit, in your main room, because it provided warmth on cold days. It was also where you did your cooking, your water boiling, your chatting, your bread toasting, your marshmallow roasting, and your sock drying. Basically, it was the center of family life.

Hestia always hung out there. She had sort of taken over

responsibility for keeping the home fires burning. It made her feel good, especially when her family gathered around for meals.

Zeus yelled, "Hey, Hestia! C'mere."

She approached his throne warily, looking at Poseidon and Apollo, who were both grinning at her, holding bouquets of flowers and boxes of candy. She thought, Uh-oh.

"Great news," Zeus said. "Both of these fine gods want to marry you. Because I'm a stand-up king and an all-around thoughtful dude, I will let you pick. Bachelor Number One, Poseidon, likes long walks on the beach and scuba diving. Bachelor Number Two, Apollo, enjoys music and poetry and spends his free time reading prophecies at the Oracle of Delphi. Who do you like better?"

Hestia sobbed in horror, which kind of surprised the bachelors. She threw herself at Zeus's feet and cried, "Please, my lord. No-o-o! Neither of them!"

Apollo frowned and checked his breath.

Poseidon wondered if he'd forgotten his underarm deodorant again.

Before they could get too angry, Hestia collected herself and tried to explain. "I have nothing against these gods," she said. "But I don't want to marry *anyone*! I want to be single forever."

Zeus scratched his head. That idea simply did not compute. "So . . . *never* get married? You don't want kids? You don't want to be a wife?"

"That's correct, my lord," Hestia said. "I—I will take care of the hearth for all time. I will tend the flames. I'll prepare the feasts. Whatever I can do to help out the family. Only, promise me I'll never have to get married!"

Apollo and Poseidon were a little miffed, but it was hard to stay mad at Hestia. She was so sweet and earnest and helpful. They forgave her for the same reasons they wanted to marry her in the first place. She was genuinely nice. Among the Olympians, niceness was a rare and valuable commodity.

"I rescind my offer of marriage," Poseidon said. "Furthermore, I will protect Hestia's right *not* to marry."

"Me, too," Apollo said. "If that's what she wants, I will honor her wishes."

Zeus shrugged. "Well, I still don't get it. But okay. She *does* keep an excellent hearth. Nobody else knows how to toast marshmallows just right—not too soft, not too crispy. Hestia, your wish is granted!"

Hestia breathed a huge sigh of relief.

She became the official goddess of the hearth, which may not seem like a big deal but was exactly what Hestia wanted. Later on, people made up a story about how Hestia used to have a throne on Mount Olympus and gave it up when a newer god named Dionysus came along. It's a good story, but it's not actually in the old myths. Hestia never wanted a throne. She was way too modest for that.

Her hearth became the calm center of the storm whenever the Olympians argued. Everyone knew the fire was neutral territory. You could go there for a time-out, a cup of nectar, or a talk with Hestia. You could catch your breath without getting accosted by anyone—kind of like "base" in a game of tag.

Hestia looked out for everyone, so everyone looked out for her.

The most famous example? One night Mother Rhea had this big party on Mount Ida to celebrate the anniversary of the

Olympians' victory over Kronos. All the gods and the friendly Titans were invited, along with dozens of nymphs and satyrs. Things got pretty wild—lots of nectar drinking, ambrosia eating, and crazy dancing with the Kouretes. The gods even convinced Zeus to tell some of his infamous satyr jokes.

Hestia wasn't used to partying so much. About three in the morning, she got light-headed from the dancing and the nectar and wandered off into the woods. She bumped into a random donkey tied to a tree; probably one of the satyrs had ridden it to the party. For some reason, Hestia found this extremely funny.

"Hello, Mr. Donkey!" She giggled. "I'm going to—*hic!*—I'm going to lie down right here and, uh, take a nap. Watch over me, okay? Okay."

The goddess fell face first in the grass and started snoring. The donkey wasn't sure what to think about that, but he kept quiet.

A few minutes later, this minor nature god named Priapus came wandering through the woods. You don't hear much about Priapus in the old stories. Frankly, he's not very important. He was a country god who protected vegetable gardens. I know—exciting, right? *Oh, great Priapus, guard my cucumbers with your mighty powers!* If you've ever seen those silly plaster garden gnomes that people put in their yards, that's a holdover from the days when people placed statues of Priapus in their gardens to protect their produce.

Anyway, Priapus was all about parties and flirting with the ladies. He'd had a lot to drink that night. He was roaming the woods looking for some unsuspecting nymph or goddess he could get cuddly with.

When he came to the clearing and saw a lovely goddess passed out in the grass, snoring alluringly in the moonlight, he thought, YES!

He sneaked up to Hestia. He didn't know which goddess she was, but he didn't really care. He was sure that if he just cuddled up next to her, she would be delighted when she woke up, because hey, who wouldn't want to get romantic with the god of vegetables?

He knelt next to her. She smelled so yummy—like wood smoke and toasted marshmallows. He ran his hand through her dark hair and said, "Hey, there, baby. What do you say we do some snuggling?"

In the darkness nearby, the donkey apparently thought that sounded like an excellent idea. He brayed, "HHAWWWWW!"

Priapus yelled, "Ahhh!!"

Hestia woke with a start, horrified to find a vegetable god leaning over her, his hand in her hair. She screamed, "HELP!"

Back at the party, the other gods heard her screaming. Immediately they dropped whatever they were doing and ran to help her—because you simply didn't mess with Hestia.

When they found Priapus, all the gods started whaling on him—throwing goblets at his head, punching him, calling him names. Priapus barely got out of there with his life.

Later, he claimed he had no idea he was flirting with Hestia. He thought she was just a nymph, or something. Still, Priapus was no longer welcome at the Olympian parties. After that, everyone became even more protective of Hestia.

Now, there's one more part of Hestia's story that's kind of important, but I'm going to have to do some speculating here, because you won't find this in the old myths.

At first, there was only one hearth in the world, and it belonged to the gods. Fire was like their trademarked property. The puny humans didn't know how to make it. They were still cowering in their caves, grunting and picking their noses and hitting each other with clubs.

The Titan Prometheus, who had made those little dudes out of clay, really felt sorry for them. After all, he'd created them to look like immortals. He was pretty sure humans were capable of *acting* like immortals, too. They just needed a little help getting started.

Whenever Prometheus visited Olympus, he watched the gods gather at Hestia's hearth. Fire was the single most important thing that made the palace a home. You could use fire to keep warm. You could cook with it. You could make hot beverages. You could light torches at night. You could play any number of funny practical jokes with the hot coals. If only humans had some fire . . .

Finally Prometheus got up his courage and spoke to Zeus.

"Hey, Lord Zeus," he said. "Uh, I thought I should show the humans how to make fire."

Zeus frowned. "Humans? You mean those dirty little guys that make funny shrieks when you step on them? Why would they need fire?"

"They could learn to be more like us," Prometheus said. "They could build houses, make cities, all sorts of things."

"That," Zeus said, "is the worst idea I've ever heard. Next, you're going to want to arm the cockroaches. Give humans fire, and they're going to take over the world. They'll get all uppity and decide they're as good as immortals. No. I absolutely forbid it."

But Prometheus couldn't let it go. He kept looking at Hestia sitting next to her hearth. He admired the way she kept the Olympian family together with her sacred fires.

It just wasn't fair, Prometheus decided. Humans deserved the same comfort.

What happened next?

Most versions of the story say that Prometheus stole hot coals from the hearth. He hid them in the hollowed stalk of a fennel plant—though you'd think somebody would notice him sneaking out of the palace with a smoldering plant that smelled like burning licorice.

None of the stories mention that Hestia helped Prometheus. But the thing is, how could she *not* have known what he was doing? She was always at the hearth. There's no way Prometheus could've stolen fire without Hestia noticing.

Personally, I think she had sympathy for Prometheus and those little humans. Hestia was kindhearted that way. I think she either helped Prometheus or at least turned a blind eye and let him steal the hot coals.

Whatever the case, Prometheus sneaked out of Olympus with his secret burning licorice stick and gave it to the humans. It took a while for them to learn how to use the hot flaming stuff without killing themselves; but finally they managed, and the idea spread like . . . well, wildfire.

Usually Zeus didn't pay much attention to what was happening down on the earth. After all, the sky was his domain. But one clear night he stood at the balcony on Mount Olympus and noticed that the world was freckled with lights—in houses, towns, even a few cities. The humans had come out of their caves.

"That little punk," Zeus grumbled. "Prometheus armed the cockroaches."

Next to him, the goddess Hera said, "Uh, what?"

"Nothing," Zeus muttered. He yelled to his guards: "Find Prometheus and get him in here. *NOW!*"

Zeus was not pleased. He didn't like it when someone disobeyed his orders, especially when that someone was a Titan whom Zeus had generously spared after the war. Zeus was *so* displeased, he decided to punish Prometheus in a way no one would ever forget. He chained the Titan to a rock on Mount Caucasus at the eastern edge of the world, then summoned a huge eagle, which was Zeus's sacred animal, to peck open Prometheus's belly and feed on his liver.

Oh, sorry. That was a little gross. I hope you weren't on your way to lunch.

Every day, the eagle would rip Prometheus open and chow down. And every night, Prometheus would heal up and grow a new liver, just in time for the eagle to show up the next morning.

The other gods and Titans got the message: *Don't disobey Zeus, or bad things will happen to you, most likely involving chains, livers, and hungry eagles.*

As for Hestia, no one accused her of anything; but she must have felt bad for Prometheus, because she made sure his sacrifice wasn't in vain. She became the goddess of *all* hearths, across the world. In every mortal home, the central fireplace was sacred to her. If you needed protection, like if someone was chasing you or beating you up, you ran to the nearest hearth and no one could touch you there. Whoever lived in that house was obligated to help if you asked for sanctuary. Families would take their important oaths on the hearth, and whenever they burned a portion of their meal as a sacrifice to the gods, part of that sacrifice went to Hestia.

As towns and cities grew, they operated just like individual homes. Each town had a central hearth that was under Hestia's protection. If you were an ambassador from another city, you always visited the hearth first to proclaim that you had come in peace. If you got in trouble and you made it to the town hearth, no one in that city could harm you. In fact, the citizens were honor-bound to protect you.

It turned out Prometheus was right. Humans *did* start acting like the gods, for better or worse. Eventually, the gods got used to this and even accepted it. The humans built temples for them, burned sweet-smelling sacrifices, and chanted about how awesome the Olympians were. That certainly helped.

Still, Zeus didn't forgive Prometheus for disobeying his orders. Eventually Prometheus got freed, but that's another story.

As for Hestia, she was able to maintain peace on Olympus most of the time—but not always.

For instance, one time her sister Demeter got so mad at her brothers, she almost caused World War Zero. . . .

DEMETER TURNS INTO GRAINZILLA

O H, YEAH. DEMETER!
Try not to get too excited, because this chapter is all about the goddess of wheat, bread, and cereal. Demeter just flat-out *rocks* when it comes to carbohydrates.

I'm not being fair to her, though.

Sure, she was the goddess of agriculture, but she had other things going for her. Among the three eldest goddesses, she was the middle sister, so she combined Hestia's sweet personality with her younger sister Hera's knockout hotness. Demeter had long blond hair the color of ripe wheat. She wore a crown of woven corn leaves—not a fashion statement most people can pull off, but she managed. She liked to adorn herself with poppies, which often grow in fields of grain—or so I'm told. I don't go walking in a lot of grain fields.

A dark robe covered her bright green dress, so whenever she moved, it looked like fresh plant shoots breaking through fertile earth. She smelled like a rainstorm over a field of jasmine.

Since Hestia decided never to get married, Demeter was the first goddess who seriously drew the attention of the guy gods. (Hera was beautiful too, but her *attitude* . . . well, we'll get to that later.)

Not only was Demeter good-looking, but she was also kindhearted (mostly), she knew how to bake awesome bread and cookies, and she cut a surprisingly warlike figure wherever she went. She rode a golden chariot pulled by twin dragons. At her side gleamed a gold sword.

In fact, one of her Greek names was Demeter Khrysaoros, meaning *the Lady with the Golden Blade*. Sounds like a good title for a martial arts movie. According to some legends, her blade was actually the scythe of Kronos, which she reforged into the world's most deadly harvesting tool. Mostly she used it for cutting wheat, but if she got angry enough, she could fight with it. . . .

Anyway, the guy gods all liked her. Zeus, Poseidon, and Hades all proposed marriage, but Demeter turned them down flat. She preferred to roam the earth, turning barren plains into fertile fields, encouraging orchards to bear fruit and flowers to bloom.

One day, Zeus got persistent. He had just divorced Themis and hadn't remarried yet. He was lonely. For whatever reason, he fixated on Demeter and decided he absolutely *had* to get with her.

He found her in a field of wheat (no surprise). Demeter

yelled at him to go away, but he just kept following her around.

"Come on!" he said. "Just one kiss. Then maybe another kiss. Then maybe—"

"No!" she shouted. "You're *so* annoying!"

"I'm the king of the universe," Zeus said. "If we got together, you'd be the queen!"

"Not interested." Demeter was tempted to draw her golden sword, but Zeus *was* the most powerful god, and people who opposed him got into a lot of trouble. (*Cough*, Like Prometheus, *cough*.) Also, her golden chariot was parked way at the other end of the field, so she couldn't just hop in and flee.

Zeus kept pestering her. "Our kids would be powerful and amazing."

"Go away."

"Hey, baby. Don't be like that."

Finally Demeter got so disgusted, she transformed herself into a serpent. She figured she could lose Zeus by hiding in the fields and slithering away.

Bad idea.

Zeus could transform into an animal too. He changed into a snake and followed her. That was easy, since snakes have a great sense of smell; and like I said earlier, Demeter had a very distinctive rainstorm-over-jasmine scent.

Demeter slithered into a hole in the dirt. Another pretty terrible idea.

Zeus slithered in after her. The tunnel was narrow, so once Zeus blocked the entrance, Demeter couldn't get out. She didn't have room to change form.

Zeus trapped her and wouldn't let her go until . . . Well, use your imagination.

Months later, Demeter gave birth to her first child—a daughter named Persephone. She was such a cute, sweet baby, Demeter *almost* forgave Zeus for tricking her into reptile hanky-panky. Almost. They didn't get married, and Zeus was a pretty neglectful dad; but still the little girl became the light of Demeter's life.

More about Persephone in a sec . . .

I'd like to say that was the only time Demeter got into a bad situation with a man. Unfortunately, it wasn't.

A few years later, Demeter took a vacation to the beach. She was walking along, enjoying the solitude and the fresh sea air, when Poseidon happened to spot her. Being a sea god, he tended to notice pretty ladies walking along the beach.

He appeared out of the waves in his best green robes, with his trident in his hand and a crown of seashells on his head. (He was sure that the crown made him look irresistible.)

"Hey, girl," he said, wiggling his eyebrows. "You must be the riptide, 'cause you sweep me off my feet."

He'd been practicing that pickup line for years. He was glad he finally got to use it.

Demeter was not impressed. "Go away, Poseidon."

"Sometimes the sea goes away," Poseidon agreed, "but it always comes back. What do you say you and me have a romantic dinner at my undersea palace?"

Demeter made a mental note not to park her chariot so far away. She really could've used her two dragons for backup. She decided to change form and get away, but she knew better than to turn into a snake this time.

I need something faster, she thought.

Then she glanced down the beach and saw a herd of wild horses galloping through the surf.

That's perfect! Demeter thought. A horse!

Instantly she became a white mare and raced down the beach. She joined the herd and blended in with the other horses.

Her plan had serious flaws. First, Poseidon could also turn into a horse, and he did—a strong white stallion. He raced after her. Second, Poseidon had *created* horses. He knew all about them and could control them.

Why would a sea god create a land animal like the horse? We'll get to that later. Anyway, Poseidon reached the herd and started pushing his way through, looking for Demeter—or rather sniffing for her sweet, distinctive perfume. She was easy to find.

Demeter's seemingly perfect camouflage in the herd turned out to be a perfect trap. The other horses made way for Poseidon, but they hemmed in Demeter and wouldn't let her move. She got so panicky, afraid of getting trampled, that she couldn't even change shape into something else. Poseidon sidled up to her and whinnied something like *Hey, beautiful. Galloping my way?*

Much to Demeter's horror, Poseidon got a lot cuddlier than she wanted.

These days, Poseidon would be arrested for that kind of behavior. I mean . . . assuming he wasn't in horse form. I don't think you can arrest a horse. Anyway, back in those days, the world was a rougher, ruder place. Demeter couldn't exactly report Poseidon to King Zeus, because Zeus was just as bad.

Months later, a very embarrassed and angry Demeter gave birth to twins. The weirdest thing? One of the babies was a goddess; the other one was a stallion. I'm not going to even *try* to figure that out. The baby girl was named Despoine, but you don't hear much about her in the myths. When she grew up, her job was looking after Demeter's temple, like the high priestess of corn magic or something. Her baby brother, the stallion, was named Arion. He grew up to be a super-fast immortal steed who helped out Hercules and some other heroes, too. He was a pretty awesome horse, though I'm not sure that Demeter was real proud of having a son who needed new horseshoes every few months and was constantly nuzzling her for apples.

At this point, you'd think Demeter would have sworn off those gross, disgusting men forever and joined Hestia in the Permanently Single Club.

Strangely, a couple of months later, she fell in love with a human prince named Iasion (pronounced EYE-son, I think). Just shows you how far humans had come since Prometheus gave them fire. Now they could speak and write. They could brush their teeth and comb their hair. They wore clothes and occasionally took baths. Some of them were even handsome enough to flirt with goddesses.

This dude Iasion (not Jason, that's a different guy) was a hero of Crete. He was handsome and well mannered, and he always looked out for his local farmers, which was a sure way to Demeter's heart. One day Iasion was out inspecting some newly plowed fields when Demeter happened by in the guise of a mortal maiden. They started talking: *Oh, I love wheat. Me, too! Wheat is the best!* Or something like that; and they fell in love.

They met in the fields several more times. For a few weeks, Demeter was head-over-heels in love. Of course, something had to go wrong. The next time Demeter visited the fields, Zeus happened to be watching from Mount Olympus. He saw Demeter getting cozy with this mortal guy—hugging and kissing and talking about wheat—and Zeus got insanely jealous.

Completely unfair, right? Zeus and Demeter weren't even together. Still, when Zeus saw a mortal hero making time with "his" girl, he blew his top.

The nice thing about getting mad at mortals—they are mortal. Which means you can kill them.

Demeter was giving Iasion a big kiss when the sky rumbled. The clouds tore open, and lightning flashed. *KER-ZAP!* Suddenly Demeter was alone in the wheat field, her clothes smoldering. A pile of hero ashes lay at her feet.

She wailed and screamed curses at Zeus, but there was nothing she could do. She sulked off to her private apartment on Mount Olympus and stayed there for months. When she finally came out, she was holding the last child she would ever bear—a boy named Pluotos. (Not Pluto. That's *another* different guy.) You don't hear much about Pluotos in the old myths either, but he became a minor god of agricultural wealth. He wandered around Greece, looking for successful farmers and rewarding them for their hard work with bags of cash—kind of like the Old MacDonald Prize Patrol.

At this point, Demeter decided enough was enough. She still had the occasional date, but she never got married, never had another kid, and her relationships with the male gods were always strained.

Her experiences also kind of soured that sweet personality of hers. You might not think a grain goddess could be scary, but *dang.* You should've seen what she did to this one dude, Erisikhthon.

I know. Stupidest name ever. I think it's pronounced Err—ISS—ick—thon, but heck, I'm just guessing. Anyway, this guy was a local prince who thought he was the coolest thing since bronze. He wanted to build himself a huge mansion with lumber from the nearby forests.

The problem? The biggest and nicest trees—the only ones he thought were good enough for his mansion—were in a grove that was sacred to Demeter. These massive oaks and poplars soared over a hundred feet tall, and each one had a nature spirit, a dryad, watching over it. The dryads would dance around, singing songs about Demeter and making flower necklaces, or whatever dryads do in their spare time.

Everybody in the whole country knew the grove was sacred to Demeter, but Eric Whatever-his-name-was—he didn't care. (You know, I think I'll just call him Eric.) So Eric got like fifty of his biggest, strongest friends together. He gave them sharp bronze axes, and they headed off to the grove.

As soon as the dryads saw them coming, they shrieked in alarm and called on Demeter to protect them.

They must've had the goddess on speed dial, because she was there in a flash.

Demeter took the form of a human maiden and appeared in the road, right in front of Eric and his army of ax-wielding goons.

"Oh, my!" she said. "Such big strong men! Where are you going?"

"Out of the way, girl," Eric grumbled. "We have some chopping to do."

"But why are you attacking these poor defenseless trees?"

"I need the lumber!" Eric bellowed. "I'm going to make the greatest mansion in the world!"

His friends cheered and waved their axes menacingly.

"You should choose other trees," Demeter said, trying to keep her cool. "This grove is sacred to Demeter."

"Bah!" Eric said. "These are the tallest trees in the land. I need *tall* trees for my great hall. My friends and I intend to feast there every night. We will have such excellent feasts, I will be famous throughout Greece!"

His friends shouted, "Yum!" and made lip-smacking noises.

"But this is the home of many innocent dryads," Demeter persisted.

"If the dryads try to stop me," Eric said, "I will cut them down too!"

Demeter clenched her jaw. "And if Demeter tries to stop you?"

Eric laughed. "Let her try. I'm not afraid of a silly *crop* goddess. Now, stand aside, or I'll chop you up as well, girl."

He shouldered the goddess aside and marched toward the largest tree—a huge white poplar. As he swung his ax, a blast of hot wind knocked him on his butt.

Demeter grew to massive height—towering above the trees like Grainzilla in her green-and-black robes, her crown of corn leaves steaming in her golden hair, her scythe blade casting a shadow across the entire group of mortals.

"SO," the giant Demeter boomed, "YOU ARE NOT AFRAID?"

Eric's fifty goons dropped their axes and ran screaming like little girls.

Eric tried to rise, but his knees were jelly. "I, uh, I just . . . uh—"

"YOU WANTED TO BE FAMOUS FOR FEAST-ING!" Demeter roared. "AND YOU *WILL* FEAST, ERISIKHTHON—EVERY NIGHT, A GREAT FEAST AS YOU INTENDED! I AM THE GODDESS OF THE HAR-VEST, THE MISTRESS OF ALL NOURISHMENT. YOU WILL EAT AND EAT FOR THE REST OF YOUR DAYS, BUT YOUR HUNGER WILL NEVER BE SATISFIED!"

Demeter disappeared in a flash of emerald light.

Poor Eric ran away whimpering, and swearing to the gods that he would never *ever* touch that sacred grove. It didn't mat-ter. That night, when he had finished his dinner, he was just as hungry as when he started. He ate a second dinner, then a third; but he felt no better. He drank like, a gallon of water; but he couldn't quench his thirst.

Within a few days, the hunger and thirst became unbear-able. He only got relief when he slept. Even then, he dreamed about food. When he woke up, he was starving again.

Eric was a rich man, but within a few weeks he had sold most of his possessions just to buy food. He ate constantly, all day every day. Nothing helped. Eventually he lost everything he owned. His friends abandoned him. He got so desperate, he even tried to sell his own daughter into slavery to get money for food. Fortunately, Demeter wasn't cruel enough to let *that* happen. The daughter pleaded for someone to rescue her, and Poseidon came to her aid. Maybe he figured he owed Demeter a favor for the horse-cuddling incident. Maybe he just didn't mind helping out a pretty mortal girl. Anyway, he took the girl under his protection and made her a housekeeper in his underwater palace. As for Erisikhthon, he wasted away and died in agony. Happy ending.

Word got around. The mortals decided that maybe they should take Demeter seriously. Anybody who controls food can bless you—or they can curse you very, very badly.

After that, Demeter figured she'd gotten her anger out of her system. She decided to relax and enjoy life, and the thing that brought her the most happiness in the world was her eldest daughter, Persephone. Oh, sure, she loved her other kids; but Persephone was her favorite.

"I'm done with drama," Demeter told herself. "I'm just going to kick back and enjoy spending time with my wonderful daughter!"

As you can probably guess, that didn't work out so well.

PERSEPHONE MARRIES HER STALKER
(OR, DEMETER, THE SEQUEL)

I HAVE TO BE HONEST. I never understood what made Persephone such a big deal. I mean, for a girl who almost destroyed the universe, she seems kind of *meh*.

Sure, she was pretty. She had her mother's long blond hair and Zeus's sky blue eyes. She didn't have a care in the world. She was sure the whole world had been invented just for her pleasure. I guess when your parents are both gods, you can come to believe that.

She loved the outdoors. She spent her days roaming the countryside with her nymph and goddess friends, wading in streams, picking flowers in sunlit meadows, eating fresh fruit right off the tree—heck, I'm just making this up, but I'm guessing that's what a teenage goddess would have done before smartphones were invented.

The thing is, Persephone didn't have much else going for

her. She wasn't all that bright. She wasn't brave. She didn't really have any goals or hobbies (other than the flower-picking thing). She was just kind of *there*, enjoying life and being a spoiled, sheltered, overprivileged kid. I guess it's nice work if you can get it, but I didn't grow up that way, so I don't have much sympathy for her.

Still, Demeter *lived* for her daughter, and I can't blame her for being over-protective. Demeter had had enough bad experiences with those sneaky male gods. After all, Persephone had come into the world because of a snake ambush. The kid was lucky she wasn't hatched from an egg.

Of course, since Persephone was declared off-limits, all the male gods noticed her and thought she was incredibly hot. They all wanted to marry her, but they knew Demeter would never allow it. Anytime one of them got close, Demeter appeared out of nowhere with her dragon-drawn chariot and her wicked golden sword.

Most of the gods let it go. They decided to find some safer goddess to date.

But one god couldn't get Persephone out of his mind—namely Hades, lord of the Underworld.

Perfect match, right? An old gloomy dude who lives in the world's largest cave filled with the souls of the dead, and he falls in love with a pretty young girl who likes sunlight and flowers and the Great Outdoors. What could possibly go wrong?

Hades knew it was hopeless. Persephone was completely out of his league. Besides, Demeter wouldn't let *any* god get close to her daughter. No way in Tartarus would she let Hades date her.

Hades tried to get over her. But he was lonely down there

in the Underworld with no company except the dead. He kept putting on his helmet of invisibility and sneaking up to the mortal world so he could watch Persephone frolic around. In other words, he was the world's first stalker.

I don't know if you've ever had a crush on somebody that bad, but Hades became obsessed. He kept sketches of Persephone in his pocket. He carved her name on his obsidian dining table with a knife—which took a lot of work. He dreamed about her and had imaginary conversations with her where he admitted his love and she confessed that she had always had a thing for creepy older guys who lived in caves full of dead people.

Hades got so distracted, he couldn't even concentrate on his work. His job was to sort out the souls of the dead once they got to the Underworld, but the ghosts started escaping back into the world, or wandering into the wrong spiritual neighborhoods. The traffic jams at the gates of the Underworld got ridiculous.

Finally Hades couldn't stand it anymore. To his credit, he didn't try to trick Persephone or take her by force—at least not at first. He thought: Well, Demeter will never listen to me. Maybe I should talk to Persephone's dad.

It wasn't easy for Hades to visit Mount Olympus. He knew he wasn't welcome there. He certainly didn't want to ask any favors of his annoying little brother Zeus, but he put on a brave face and marched into the Olympian throne room.

He happened to catch Zeus in a good mood. The lord of the skies had just finished all his godly work for the week—scheduling the clouds, organizing the winds, and doing whatever else a sky god has to do. Now he was sitting back, drinking some nectar, and enjoying the gorgeous day. He was daydreaming about another beautiful lady he was intent on marrying, namely Hera; so when Hades came to see him, Zeus had a faraway smile on his face.

"Lord Zeus." Hades bowed.

"Hades!" Zeus cried. "What's up, man? Long time no see!"

Hades was tempted to remind Zeus that it was "long time, no see" because Zeus had told him he wasn't welcome on Mount Olympus; but he decided he'd better not mention that.

"Uh, actually . . ." Hades tugged nervously at his black robes. "I need some advice. About a woman."

Zeus grinned. "You've come to the right place. The ladies love me!"

"Okay . . ." Hades started to wonder if this was a good idea. "It's about one particular lady—your daughter, Persephone."

Zeus's smile wavered. "Say what, now?"

Hades had been holding in his feelings for so long, he just broke down. He confessed everything, even the stalkerish stuff. He promised he would make Persephone an excellent husband. He would be devoted and give her everything she wanted, if only Zeus would give him permission to marry her.

Zeus stroked his beard. Most days, he would have gotten angry at such a ridiculous request. He would've brought out his lightning bolts and sent Hades back to the Underworld with his robes on fire and his hair all spiky and smoking. But today Zeus was in a good mood. He was actually sort of touched that Hades had come to him with this problem and been so honest. He felt sorry for his creepy stalker brother, and he *definitely* understood how a guy could get obsessed with a woman.

Sure, Persephone was his daughter; but Zeus had *lots* of

daughters by lots of different ladies. It wasn't like Persephone was his special favorite, or anything. He was inclined to be generous and give her away.

He drummed his fingers on the arm of his throne. "The problem is Demeter. Uh . . . that *is* Demeter's daughter, right? I forget."

"Yes, my lord," Hades said.

"Her favorite daughter," Zeus remembered. "The light of her life, whom she never lets out of her sight, et cetera."

"Yes, my lord." Hades started to feel uncomfortable. "Should I talk to Demeter? Perhaps if you broke the ice and made her promise to listen. Or maybe I should declare my love to Persephone?"

"What?" Zeus looked appalled. "Be honest with women? That never works, bro. You've got to be strong. Take what you want."

"Uh . . . really?"

"Always works for me," Zeus said. "I suggest kidnapping. When nobody is looking, capture Persephone and take her back to your crib. Demeter won't know what happened. By the time she figures it out . . . too late! Persephone will be yours. You'll have plenty of time to convince the young lady to stay with you in the Underworld."

Hades was starting to have doubts about Zeus's wisdom. "Um, you're sure this is a good idea?"

"Totally!" Zeus said.

Hades chewed his lip. The whole kidnapping thing seemed a little risky. He wasn't sure if Persephone would actually like being abducted, but he didn't know much about women. Maybe Zeus was right.

(For the record: NO, HE WASN'T.)

"There's one problem, my lord," Hades said. "Persephone is never alone. She's either with Demeter or with some nymph or goddess chaperones. How can I abduct her in secret? Even if I use my invisibility helmet, I can't turn *her* invisible or stop her from screaming."

Zeus's eyes twinkled mischievously. "Leave that to me. Go get your chariot ready."

Zeus waited until Demeter was busy doing some agricultural stuff on the far side of the world—like ripening the barley in Libya, or something. I'm not sure what.

Anyway, Persephone was left in the care of her nymph chaperones. Usually that worked out fine, but the nymphs weren't really cut out to be bodyguards. They could be easily distracted, and so could Persephone.

As usual, the girls went out into the meadows. They spent the morning exploring the hills and having splash-fights in the river. After a nice lazy lunch, letting their dresses dry in the sunlight, Persephone decided to go pick some flowers.

"Don't wander too far!" one of the nymphs called.

"I won't," Persephone promised.

She wasn't worried. The world was her playground! Everyone loved her, and besides, what could possibly go wrong while she was picking flowers in a meadow?

The nymphs were sleepy and warm and full from lunch, and so they lay down for a nap.

Persephone roamed the hillside until she'd gathered an entire bouquet from the nearest rosebushes. For some reason, the roses didn't even have thorns. Their intoxicating smell made

Persephone giddy. She traipsed a little farther away and spotted a whole field of violets.

"Oh, pretty!"

She wandered through the violets, picking the best ones and dropping the roses, because they now seemed pale in comparison.

Well, you can probably see where this is going, but Persephone was clueless. She didn't realize Zeus was causing these flowers to grow—making each batch more colorful and fragrant than the last, leading Persephone farther and farther away from her chaperones.

So how could Zeus, a sky god, make flowers grow? Dunno. Best guess: he still had some pull with Gaea the Earth Mother, even though she was asleep. I'm thinking Zeus could occasionally summon her power to make things happen on the earth— maybe not huge things, like creating mountains. But making flowers grow? Not a big deal.

Persephone wandered from flower patch to flower patch, murmuring, "Ooh, pretty! Ooh, pretty!" as she picked her favorites.

Before she realized it, she was miles away from her sleeping nymph friends. She meandered into a secluded valley filled with hyacinths.

She was reaching down to pick a beautiful red one when the ground rumbled. A chasm opened at her feet, and four black horses pulling a massive chariot thundered into the sunlight. The driver was dressed in dark flowing robes. He wore iron gloves, with a huge sword at his side and a whip in his hand. His face was covered with an elaborate bronze helmet engraved with images of death and torture.

In retrospect, Hades wondered if it was such a good idea to wear his helmet of terror on a first date, but by then it was too late.

Persephone screamed and fell backward into the grass.

She should have run, but she was in shock. She couldn't even fathom what was happening. Everything had always revolved around her, gone her way. She *couldn't* be in danger. But she was pretty sure she hadn't wished for a demonic-looking guy in a giant black chariot to come and trample her hyacinths.

Truth be told, she'd occasionally had daydreams about some handsome young man sweeping her off her feet. She and the nymphs had spent a lot of time giggling about that.

But this was *not* what she'd envisioned.

Hades took off his helm. His complexion was even paler than usual. He had a bad case of helmet-hair. He was sweating and nervous and blinking like he had something in his eyes.

"I am Hades," he said in a squeaky voice. "I love you."

Persephone screamed again, much louder.

Not knowing what else to do, Hades grabbed her arm, pulled her into the chariot, and spurred his horses. His dark ride disappeared into the earth. The chasm closed up behind him.

The only person who actually saw the kidnapping was the Titan Helios, way up in his chick-magnet sun chariot, because he had a great view and could see pretty much everything. But do you think he got on the phone to Olympus to report a kidnapping?

Nope. First, they didn't have phones. Second, Helios didn't like to get involved with godly dramas. He was a Titan, after all. He figured he was lucky just to have a job and not get thrown into Tartarus. Also, this kidnapping wasn't the craziest thing he'd seen while crossing the sky every day. Those gods were always doing wild things. Man, the stories he could tell. Someday he should write a book.

So Helios continued on his way.

As for the nymphs who were supposed to be watching Persephone, they slept right through the abduction. The only person who heard Persephone screaming was the most unlikely person you could imagine.

In a cave on a nearby mountainside, a Titan named Hecate was minding her own business. Hecate was into magic and spooky nighttime crossroads and ghosts. She was sort of the first super-fan of Halloween. Normally she only left her cave after dark, so that day she was sitting inside reading spell books or whatever when she heard a girl screaming.

Hecate may have been a dark goddess of magic, but she wasn't evil. She immediately ran to help. By the time she got to the meadow, the action was over.

Hecate's magic was weak in the daytime. She could tell that the earth had opened and somebody had been snatched up in a chariot and dragged underground, but Hecate had no idea who was the kidnapper and who was the kidnapee.

Hecate wasn't sure what to do. It wasn't like she could call 911. Since she didn't know the facts, she decided to go back to her cave and wait until nightfall, when she could cast better spells and hopefully get more information.

Meanwhile, the nymphs woke from their nap and went looking for Persephone, but she had literally vanished off the face of the earth. The nymphs were starting to panic by the time Demeter returned and found out her precious daughter was missing. I'm not sure what Demeter did to punish those nymphs, but it could not have been good.

Anyway, Demeter was freaked. She wandered around shouting for Persephone until her voice got hoarse. She asked everyone she met if they had seen anything.

For *nine days* Demeter didn't change her clothes or take a bath. She didn't eat or sleep. She did nothing but look for Persephone. She must have started searching in the wrong direction, because on the tenth day she finally circled back around and combed the area near Hecate's cave.

Hecate heard Demeter calling for Persephone. Immediately the magic goddess put two and two together. Every night, Hecate had been trying to figure out what the abduction was all about, but her spells weren't telling her anything. Some strong magic was at work, covering up the kidnapping. Hecate had a feeling a powerful god was behind it—or maybe more than one.

Hecate ran down to meet Demeter. She told the grain goddess about the screaming she'd heard, and her belief that some unknown god had kidnapped Persephone.

The distraught mom didn't take the news well. She shrieked so loudly that all the plants within a five-mile radius withered and died. For hundreds of miles in each direction, every ear of corn on the Greek mainland exploded into popcorn.

"I will find whoever has taken her!" Demeter wailed. "I will murder him! Then I will murder him again!"

At this point, most folks would've backed away from the crazy lady, but Hecate felt bad for her.

"I'll help you search tonight," she told Demeter. "I've got torches, and I'm really good at seeing in the dark."

They searched from dusk until dawn but had no luck.

Hecate went back to her cave to rest, promising to help again after nightfall, but Demeter couldn't stop.

She stumbled on alone until evening fell and she came to a kingdom called Eleusis. At this point, even the immortal goddess was getting exhausted. She decided to visit the town, maybe rest her feet for a few minutes and mingle with the locals. Perhaps they had seen something or heard some news.

Demeter disguised herself as an old mortal woman. She made her way to the town's central hearth, because that's where strangers normally went when they wanted to ask the locals for assistance. A crowd had gathered in the square. A lady with fine robes and a golden crown was making some kind of speech. Being an intelligent goddess, Demeter thought: She must be the queen.

It turned out Queen Metaneira was there with her family and her household guards, offering sacrifices to the gods in celebration of the birth of her newest son, Demophoon. (Or maybe she was there to apologize to the gods for giving her son such a dumb name.) Anyway, when Demeter walked up, Queen Metaneira was just offering a prayer to Demeter. Even in Demeter's desperate state of mind, that must've been sort of a rush, hearing somebody praying to her when they didn't know she was in the crowd.

If it were me, I'd wait until the queen said, "O great Demeter—"

Then I'd jump out with a bunch of explosions and fireworks and say, "YOU CALLED?"

Probably a good thing nobody has made me a god.

At any rate, Demeter figured this was a good omen. She

waited for the queen to finish blessing her new baby, who was very cute. As the crowd broke up, Demeter made her way toward the queen; but Metaneira noticed her first.

"Old woman!" called the queen.

Demeter blinked. She looked around, wondering who Metaneira was talking to. Then she remembered she was in disguise.

"Oh, right! Yes, my queen!" Demeter said in her best old-lady voice.

The queen studied Demeter's face and her ragged clothes. Even in disguise, Demeter must have looked weary. After ten days, she didn't smell nearly as jasmine sweet as usual.

"I do not know you," the queen decided. Her family and retainers gathered around.

Demeter wondered if she was going to have to turn into a hundred-foot-tall grain monster and scare them away, but the queen only smiled. "Welcome to Eleusis! We always greet strangers, because you never know when one of them might be a god in disguise, eh?"

The queen's guards chuckled. They were probably thinking: Yeah, right. This old lady a goddess.

Demeter bowed. "Very wise, my queen. Very wise indeed."

"Do you need a place to stay?" the queen asked. "Do you require food? How may we help you?"

Wow, Demeter thought. She's *serious*.

After days of anxiety, running frantically around Greece looking for her daughter, Demeter was dumbstruck to receive such kindness. These puny mortals didn't know her from any ordinary beggar—yet the queen herself took time to be nice to her, nicer in fact than most of Demeter's fellow gods would have been.

Demeter felt so tired and emotionally spent that she burst into tears. "My daughter," she sobbed. "My daughter has been stolen from me."

The queen gasped. "What? This is an outrage!"

A handsome young man stepped forward and took Demeter's hands. "Old woman, I am Triptolemus, the first-born son of the queen. I pledge that I will help you find your daughter, however I can!"

Queen Metaneira nodded in agreement. "But come, dear guest. You are clearly exhausted. It won't help your daughter if you kill yourself with weariness and hunger while trying to find her. Please stay in my palace tonight. Tell us your story. Rest and eat. In the morning, we will decide how best to help you."

Demeter wanted to decline. She wanted to keep going. Since she was immortal, she obviously wasn't in danger of dying. But she *was* tired. These people were nice. And after ten days on the road, her filthy clothes were starting to sprout types of mold and fungus even the *plant* goddess didn't recognize.

She thanked the queen and accepted her hospitality.

After taking a nice hot bath and putting on some new clothes, Demeter felt much better. She joined the royal family for dinner and told them of her troubles, though she left out some minor details, such as being a goddess. She explained that her daughter had disappeared while on a day trip in the meadow with her friends. A woman who lived nearby had heard screaming, so it was clear her daughter had been kidnapped, but Demeter had no idea who had taken her or where she might be.

The royal family brainstormed some helpful suggestions: offering a reward, putting Persephone's face on milk cartons, stapling MISSING posters around town. Finally Triptolemus had the winning idea.

"I will send riders in all four directions," he said. "We will gather news and spread word of this abduction. Stay with us and rest a few days, honored guest. I know you are anxious, but this is the quickest way to search the countryside. When my riders return, we will know more."

Again, Demeter wanted to protest. She was worried sick about her daughter, but she couldn't think of a better idea, and she was grateful for this family's hospitality. Also, she *could* use a few days' rest.

Since her initial panic after the abduction, Demeter's mood had started to shift to cold determination. In her heart, she knew Persephone was still out there—captured, but unharmed. Her motherly instincts told her so. No matter how long it took, Demeter would find her. And when she got her hands on the kidnapper . . . oh, her vengeance would be terrible. She would cover him in fertilizer, cause barley to sprout from all his pores, and laugh at his terrified screams as he transformed into the world's largest Chia Pet.

Demeter smiled at Prince Triptolemus. "Thank you for your kindness. I accept your offer."

"Excellent!"

"Goo," said the newborn child Demophoon, gurgling contentedly in the queen's arms.

Demeter gazed at the baby boy. Her heart filled with warmth and nostalgia. It seemed like just last century Persephone had been that small!

"Let me repay your kindness," Demeter told the queen. "I'm an excellent nursemaid, and I know what it's like being a new mom. You could use some sleep! Let me take care of your baby tonight. I promise to keep him safe. I'll bless him with special charms against evil so he'll grow up to be a strong, handsome hero!"

I've never been a mom, but I think I'd be pretty suspicious if some old lady off the street offered to watch my baby for the night. As you can probably tell, though, Queen Metaneira was a kindhearted, trusting person. She felt terrible for this old woman who had just lost her daughter. Also, it was true that Metaneira hadn't been sleeping much since the baby came along.

"I would be honored," the queen said, handing Demophoon to Demeter.

That night, the goddess rocked the baby by the fire. She sang him nursery songs from Mount Olympus, like "The Itsy-Bitsy Satyr" and "I'm a Little Cyclops." She fed Demophoon nectar, the drink of the gods, mixed with his regular milk. She whispered powerful blessings to keep him safe.

I will make you immortal, little one, Demeter thought. *It's the least I can do for your kind mother. I will make you so strong no one will ever abduct you the way my poor daughter was abducted.*

When the child dozed off, Demeter placed him in the blazing fireplace.

You're probably thinking: *Ah! She roasted the little dude?*

No, it's cool. The kid was fine.

Demeter's magic protected him, so the flames only felt warm and pleasant. As Demophoon slept, the fire began burning away his mortal essence, starting the process that would turn him into a god.

In the morning, Queen Metaneira couldn't believe how much her baby had grown. He'd put on several pounds overnight. His eyes were brighter and his grip was stronger.

"What did you feed him?" the queen asked in amazement.

Demeter chuckled. "Oh, nothing special, but I did promise to look out for him. He's going to be a fine young man!"

At breakfast, Triptolemus announced that his riders had already left. He expected news in the next day or two. Demeter was anxious. She was half-tempted to keep traveling on her own, but she agreed to wait for the riders to return.

That night, Demeter again took charge of the baby Demophoon. She fed him more ambrosia and laid him down to sleep in fire. In the morning, she was pleased to see that he was immortalizing nicely.

"One more night ought to do it," she decided.

When she gave the child back to the queen at breakfast, Metaneira wasn't so thrilled. Her boy suddenly looked like a four-month-old rather than a newborn. She wondered what kind of magic Demeter was using, and whether it had passed the safety test for babies. Maybe the old lady was slipping some kind of growth hormone into Demophoon's milk. In a few more days, the kid might have six-pack abs and hairy armpits.

Still, the queen was too polite to yell at her guest or throw accusations with no proof. She kept her doubts to herself. Secretly she hoped the riders would come back today, and the old lady would be on her way.

Unfortunately, the riders didn't return.

"I'm sure they'll be back in the morning," Triptolemus promised. "Then we should have more information."

Demeter agreed to stay one more night. This time, when

dinner was finished, she took the baby from the queen without even asking, just assuming it was okay. Metaneira's heart hammered in her rib cage. She watched Demeter carry Demophoon back to her guest room, and the queen tried to convince herself everything was fine. The old lady was harmless. She would *not* turn her newborn son into a 'roid-raging monster overnight.

But the queen couldn't sleep.

She worried that she was going to miss her baby's entire childhood. She would wake up in the morning and see this big bulky three-year-old with facial hair running toward her, shouting in a deep voice, "Hey, Mom! What up?"

Finally Metaneira couldn't stand it anymore. She crept down the hall to Demeter's room to check on the baby.

The bedroom door was open just a crack. Firelight glowed at the sill. Metaneira heard the old woman singing a lullaby inside, but the baby wasn't making a sound. Hopefully that was good. He was sleeping peacefully. But what if he was in danger?

Without knocking, she opened the door . . . then screamed at the top of her lungs. The old lady was sitting calmly in a rocking chair, watching baby Demophoon burn in the fire!

Metaneira charged to the fireplace. She snatched the baby out of the flames, heedless of how much it burned her hands and arms. The baby started wailing, unhappy about waking up from a nice warm nap.

Metaneira wheeled on Demeter, ready to chew her face off, but the old lady yelled at her *first*.

"What are you THINKING?" Demeter shouted, rising from her chair with her fists clenched. "Why did you do that? You've ruined everything!"

Metaneira was stunned speechless. Meanwhile, Prince

Triptolemus and several guards stumbled into the room to investigate the screaming.

"What's wrong?" Triptolemus demanded.

"Arrest this woman!" Metaneira shrieked, clutching her baby in her blistered arms. "She tried to kill Demophoon! He was burning in the fireplace!"

The guards surged forward, but Triptolemus yelled, "WAIT!"

The guards hesitated.

Triptolemus frowned at his mother, then at the old woman. He was smart enough to realize something wasn't right here. The baby was crying, but otherwise he seemed fine. He didn't look burned. The blanket wasn't even singed. The old woman looked more exasperated than guilty or scared.

"What is the meaning of this?" he asked their guest.

"The meaning," growled Demeter, "is that your mother just *ruined* things for the baby."

The old woman began to glow. Her disguise burned away and she stood before them as a golden-haired goddess, her robes shimmering with green light, her scythe sword glinting at her side.

The guards dropped their weapons and retreated. Maybe they'd heard the story of Eric.

The queen gasped. As a pious woman, she knew how to spot her gods. "Demeter!"

"Yes," said the goddess. "I was *trying* to do you a favor, you silly woman. A few more hours in the fire, and your baby boy would have been immortal! He would've grown into a fine young god and brought you eternal honor. Now you've ruined the magic. He will simply be human—a great hero, yes, strong and tall, but doomed to a mortal life. He will only be Demophoon, when he could have been Fully Phoon! Phoon the Great!"

Metaneira gulped. She wasn't sure if she should apologize, or thank the goddess, or what. She was so relieved to have her baby back safely, unburned and without hairy pits, that she didn't really care whether he was immortal. A great hero sounded good enough for her. Still, she didn't think she should say that to the goddess.

"I—I should have trusted you," Metaneira murmured. "Please, great Demeter, punish me for my lack of faith, but do not harm my family."

Demeter waved her comment aside. "Don't be silly. I won't punish you. I'm just annoyed. You've been helpful in my search, and—"

"Oh!" Triptolemus raised his hand like he had a burning question.

"Yes?" Demeter asked.

"That reminds me," Triptolemus said. "One of my riders just returned with news."

"About my daughter?" Demeter completely forgot her annoyance and grabbed the prince's shoulders. "Have you found her?"

Triptolemus wasn't used to being shaken by an immortal goddess, but he tried to keep his cool. "Uh, not exactly, my lady. However, the rider says he met someone who met someone who met a guy in a tavern far to the east. This guy claimed he was the Titan of the sun, Helios. He was trying to impress the women with his stories, apparently."

Demeter narrowed her eyes. "Flirting with random women

in a tavern? That sounds like Helios. Well, it sounds like most of the gods, actually. What did he say?"

"Apparently he was telling a story about your daughter Persephone. He claimed that he saw the abduction and he knew who did it. But, er, he didn't name the culprit."

"Of course!" Demeter got so excited that grass started to sprout on Triptolemus's shirt. "Oh, sorry . . . but this is excellent news! I should've thought to visit Helios sooner. He sees everything!"

She kissed Triptolemus on the cheek. "Thank you, my dear boy. I will not forget your help. Once I reclaim my daughter, I will reward you handsomely."

Triptolemus tried to smile but failed. He was worried Demeter was going to make him sleep in a burning fireplace. "That's okay. Really."

"No, I insist. But now I must fly!"

Demeter turned into a turtledove, which was one of her sacred birds, and flew out the window, leaving behind the very confused royal family of Eleusis.

Helios knew he was in trouble as soon as Demeter burst into his throne room. The sun Titan always liked to relax in the last hours of the night, before he had to saddle his fiery horses and get to work.

He was kicking back, thinking about all the crazy stuff he'd seen during his ride the day before. He really *should* write a book. Then suddenly, the bronze doors of his audience chamber flew open, and Demeter rode her dragon-drawn chariot right up the steps of his throne. The dragons snarled and bared their fangs, drooling all over Helios's golden shoes.

"Uh, hi?" he said nervously.

"Where is my daughter?" Demeter's voice was calm and deadly serious.

Helios winced. He didn't want to get involved in godly disagreements. They didn't pay him enough for that. But he decided that right now was *not* the time to withhold information.

"Hades took her," he said. He told her everything he'd seen.

Demeter held back a scream. She didn't want to cause another popcorn epidemic. But *Hades*? Of all the disgusting, horrible male gods who might have taken her precious daughter, Hades was the most disgusting and horrible of all.

"And *why* didn't you tell me this sooner?" Her voice was as sharp as her scythe.

"Well, um—"

"Never mind!" she snapped. "I'll deal with you later. When Zeus hears how Hades has dishonored our daughter, he'll be furious!"

She rode out of the sun palace and made straight for Mount Olympus.

As you can guess, her conversation with Zeus didn't go quite the way she planned. She marched into the throne room and yelled, "Zeus! You won't believe what happened."

She told him the whole story and demanded he do something.

Strangely, Zeus did *not* seem furious. He wouldn't meet Demeter's eyes. He kept picking at the end of his lightning bolt. Sweat trickled down the side of his face.

A cold feeling came over Demeter—a kind of anger that was much deeper than anything she'd felt before.

"Zeus, what did you do?"

"Well . . ." Zeus shrugged sheepishly. "Hades might have mentioned that he wanted to marry Persephone."

Demeter's fingernails dug into her palms until her hands were dripping golden ichor. "And?"

"And it's a good match! Hades is powerful. He's handsome . . . or, um, well, he's *powerful.*"

"I want my daughter back," Demeter said. "NOW."

Zeus squirmed on his throne. "Look, babe—"

"Do NOT call me babe."

"I can't go back on my word. It's done. She's down in the Underworld. They're married. End of story."

"No," Demeter said. *"Not* the end of the story. Until I have my daughter back, *nothing* will grow on the earth. Crops will die. People will starve. Every single living creature will share my pain until *you* do the right thing and return Persephone!"

Demeter thundered out of the room. (Thundering was usually Zeus's job, but she was beyond mad.) She went back to Eleusis, the one kingdom where people had helped her. She allowed the crops there to continue growing, but on the rest of the earth, everything withered and died just as she'd threatened.

Zeus told himself, *She's just throwing a tantrum. Give her a few days and she'll get over it.*

Weeks passed. Then months. Humans starved by the thousands. And when humans starved, they couldn't make burnt offerings to the gods. They couldn't build new temples. All they could do was cry out in agony, praying to the gods twenty-four/seven, *Help us! We're starving!* Which gave Zeus a *huge* headache.

Also, the gods were reduced to eating ambrosia and nectar,

which got old quickly. Without grain, they couldn't have any bread or those awesome fresh-baked brownies that Hera sometimes made.

Finally Zeus relented. He summoned his main messenger, a god named Hermes, and said, "Hey, Hermes, go down to the Underworld. Tell Hades he's got to send Persephone back right away or we'll never have any peace—or brownies."

"On it, boss." Hermes zoomed down to the Underworld.

Meanwhile, Persephone had been in the palace of Hades this whole time, and she was learning the hard way that the world did *not* revolve around her.

No matter how many times she stamped her feet, held her breath, or screamed for her mother, she couldn't get what she wanted.

She threw some epic tantrums. She tore up her bed (which made it hard to sleep); she kicked the walls (which hurt her foot); and when Hades's ghostly servants brought her meals, she smashed the plates and refused to eat anything, even though she was starving.

The "not eating" thing was important. See, in Greek times, eating food in another person's house was like signing a contract. It meant you accepted your place as their guest. They had to treat you properly, but you also had to behave properly. Basically, it meant you and your host were on friendly terms.

Persephone didn't want to sign that contract. Not at all.

The first few days, she refused to leave her room. Hades didn't force her to, though he tried to talk to her a few times.

"Look," he said, "your dad agreed to the marriage. I'm

sorry about the whole kidnapping thing—which by the way was *his* idea—but honestly, I *love* you. You're amazing and beautiful and I promise—"

"Get out!" She threw whatever she could grab—which happened to be a pillow. The pillow bounced off Hades's chest.

Hades looked sad and left her alone.

Around the fourth day, Persephone got bored and left her room. No one stopped her. She quickly realized why. Outside of the king's palace, there was no place to go. She was stuck in the Underworld, with nothing in any direction except gray gloomy plains filled with dead people, and no sky above except dark mist.

Even if she ran away from the palace, she didn't want to walk through those fields full of dead souls, and she had no idea how to get back to the upper world.

The most infuriating thing? Hades *refused* to get mad at her, no matter how many plates she smashed or sheets she tore up, or how many horrible names she called him—though honestly she didn't know that many insults. She'd lived a happy, sheltered life, and calling Hades *Stupid Head* didn't quite seem forceful enough.

Hades took her abuse and told her he was sorry that she was angry.

"I do love you," he promised. "You are the brightest thing in the entire Underworld. With you here, I will never miss the sunlight again. You are warmer than the sun by far."

"You're a stupid head!" she screamed.

After he left, she realized that what he'd said was sort of sweet—but only in a creepy, pathetic way, of course.

The days passed. The more Persephone wandered through

the palace, the more amazed she became. The mansion was *huge.*
Hades had entire rooms made of gold and silver. Every day, his
servants set out new bouquets of flowers made from precious
jewels: a dozen ruby roses on diamond stems, platinum and
gold sunflowers with emerald-studded leaves. Even on Mount
Olympus, Persephone had never seen such dazzling wealth.

She started to realize that as creepy and horrible as Hades
was, he had tremendous power. He controlled thousands of
souls. He commanded horrifying monsters and creatures of
the darkness. He had access to all the wealth under the earth,
making him the richest god in the world. No matter what
Persephone destroyed, he could instantly replace it with something even better.

Still, she hated the place. Of course she did! She missed the
sun and the meadows and the fresh flowers. The Underworld
was so clammy she could never get warm. The constant gloom
gave her a serious case of seasonal affective disorder.

Then one day she stumbled across Hades's throne room.
He was sitting at the far end, on a throne sculpted from thousands of bones, talking to a shimmering ghost. Persephone
guessed it was a soul newly arrived from the mortal world, as it
seemed to be giving Hades the latest news.

"Thank you," Hades told the spirit. "But I will never give
in! I don't care *how* many mortals die!"

Persephone marched up to the dais. "What are you talking
about, you horrible person? Who are you killing now?"

Hades looked stunned. He waved at the ghost and it
disappeared.

"I—I don't want to tell you," Hades said. "It would bring
you pain."

Which only made her want to know more. "What's going on?"

Hades took a deep breath. "Your mother is angry. She knows now that I took you for my wife."

"Ha!" Persephone's heart soared. "Oh, you're in so much trouble. She's on her way down here right now with an army of angry nymphs and grain spirits, isn't she?"

"No," Hades said.

Persephone blinked. "No?"

"She will not cross into the Underworld," Hades said. "She *hates* it here. She hates me."

"Of course she does!" Persephone said, though she was a little disappointed. She'd been counting on her mom to rescue her. Surely Demeter would come get her personally, whether or not she hated the Underworld. "But . . . I'm confused. What were you saying about mortals dying?"

Hades grimaced. "Your mother is trying to force Zeus into getting you back. Demeter is starving the entire world, letting thousands of people die until you are returned to her."

Persephone almost fell over. Her mother was doing *what*?

Demeter had always been so gentle and kind. Persephone couldn't imagine her mom letting a corn plant die, much less thousands of people. But something told her that Hades wasn't lying.

Persephone's eyes stung. She wasn't sure if she was sad or angry or just sick to her stomach. Thousands of mortals were dying because of *her*?

"You must return me," Persephone said. "Immediately."

Hades clenched his jaw. For the first time he didn't look

mopey or weak. He met her gaze. His dark eyes flared with purple fire.

"You are my very existence now," Hades said. "You are more precious to me than all the jewels under the earth. I'm sorry you do not love me, but I will be a good husband to you. I'll do everything I can to make you happy. I will *not* return you. If I must, I will counter Demeter's attack. I will open the gates of the Underworld and let the dead flood back into the world rather than release you!"

Persephone didn't know what to do with that information. Her heart felt like it was compressing into a tiny jewel, as bright and hard as a diamond.

She turned and fled. She ran down a corridor she'd never explored before, opened a doorway, and stepped out into . . . a garden.

She couldn't breathe. It was the most incredible place she had ever seen. Ghostly warm lights floated overhead—perhaps the souls of particularly sunny dead people? She wasn't sure, but the garden was warmer and brighter than anywhere else in the Underworld. Beautiful subterranean flowers glowed in the dark. Orchards of carefully pruned trees bore sweet-smelling blooms and neon-bright fruit.

The paths were sculpted with rubies and topaz. White birch trees soared into the air like frozen ghosts. A brook wended through the middle of the garden. On a nearby table sat a silver tray with a frosted decanter of nectar, along with Persephone's favorite cookies and fresh fruits.

She couldn't understand what she was seeing. All the flowers and trees she loved best from the upper world were here in this garden, somehow blooming and flourishing in the darkness.

"What . . . ?" She couldn't form a sentence. "How—"

"Do you like it?" Hades spoke just behind her. He'd followed her outside, and for once his voice didn't make her cringe.

She turned and saw a tiny smile on his face. He didn't look so horrible when he smiled.

"You—you did this for me?"

He shrugged. "I'm sorry it wasn't ready sooner. I gathered the best gardeners in the Underworld. Askalaphos! Where are you?"

A thin young man appeared from the bushes. He had gardening shears in his hand. He was obviously one of the dead, judging from his papery skin and the yellowish tinge in his eyes, but he managed a smile. He somehow looked more alert than the other zombies Persephone had met.

"Just pruning the roses, my lord," said Askalaphos. "My lady, a pleasure to meet you."

Persephone knew she should say something, like *hello*, but she was too stunned.

Just then a winged gargoyle flew into the garden. It whispered something in Hades's ear, and the god's face grew stern. "A visitor," he said. "Excuse me, my dear."

When he was gone, Askalaphos gestured to the patio table. "My lady, would you like something to eat?"

"No," Persephone said automatically. Despite everything, she knew she shouldn't accept the hospitality of a god who had kidnapped her.

"Suit yourself," said the gardener. "I just picked these ripe pomegranates, though. They're amazing."

He pulled one from his coveralls and set it on the table,

then cut the fruit into three parts with his knife. Hundreds of juicy purple-red seeds glistened inside.

Now personally, I'm not a big pomegranate fan, but Persephone loved them. They reminded her of her happiest moments aboveground, frolicking in the meadows with her nymph friends.

She looked at the luscious fruit, and her stomach howled in protest. It had been days since she'd eaten anything. She was immortal, so she couldn't die; but she *felt* like she was starving.

A little bite won't hurt, she told herself.

She sat down, put one seed in her mouth, and couldn't believe how good it tasted. Before she knew it, she had eaten a third of the fruit. She probably would've eaten more if Hades hadn't returned with his visitor—the god Hermes.

"My love!" Hades called, and his voice sounded like he'd been weeping.

Persephone shot to her feet. She hid her sticky purple fingers behind her and hoped she didn't have juice running down her chin. "Mmm-hmm?" she mumbled, working a few half-chewed seeds around in her mouth.

"This is Hermes." Hades's face looked broken with despair. "He—he has come to take you back."

Persephone swallowed. "But . . . you said—"

"Zeus commands it." Hades sounded so sad that Persephone forgot this was good news. "I would gladly fight any god for your sake, but even I cannot fight against the entire Olympian council. I am . . . I am forced to give you up."

Persephone should have been shouting with joy. This was what she wanted! So why did she feel so bad about it? She couldn't stand the look of devastation on Hades's face. He'd made this garden just for her. He'd treated her well . . . at least after the initial kidnapping, and that had been *Zeus's* idea. Hades had been ready to open the gates of the dead for her sake.

Hermes didn't seem bothered by any of that. "Well, excellent!" He grinned at Persephone. "Ready to go? Just some regulation questions I have to ask first—you know, customs stuff for crossing the border. Have you come into contact with any live animals?"

Persephone frowned. "No."

"Visited any farms?" Hermes inquired. "Are you carrying more than ten thousand drachmas in foreign currency?"

"Uh . . . no."

"Last question," Hermes said. "Have you eaten any food in the Underworld?" He held up his hands in apology. "I know it's a stupid question. I mean, obviously you're smarter than that. If you ate any food in the Underworld, you'd have to stay here forever!"

Persephone cleared her throat. "Uh . . ."

I don't know if she would've lied or not, but before she could answer, the gardener Askalaphos said, "Show them your hands, my lady."

Persephone blushed. She held out her hands, which were stained purple. "One third of a pomegranate," she said. "That's all."

"Oh," Hermes said. "Whoops."

"She can stay!" Hades danced in a circle, grinning from ear to ear, then seemed to realize he didn't look very dignified. "Er, I mean, she *must* stay. I'm—I'm sorry, my dear, if that makes you sad. But I can't pretend I'm not delighted. This is wonderful news."

Persephone's emotions were so jumbled that she wasn't sure *how* she felt.

Hermes scratched his head. "This complicates things. I've got to report for new orders. Back soon."

He flew to Mount Olympus and told the other gods his news.

When Demeter heard the problem, she flew into a rage. Somehow she managed to send a powerful curse straight through the ground, into that Underworld garden in Hades's mansion. She zapped the gardener Askalaphos into a gecko because he'd told on Persephone.

Why a gecko? I have no idea. I guess, off the top of her head, a zombie gecko was the worst curse she could think of.

Demeter threatened to let the world keep starving unless she got her daughter back. Hades sent a new message via Hermes, warning that the dead would rise in a zombie apocalypse unless Persephone stayed with him. Zeus was getting a splitting headache, imagining his beautiful world being ripped apart, until Hestia came up with a solution.

"Let Persephone divide her time," suggested the hearth goddess. "She ate one third of the pomegranate. Let her spend a third of the year with Hades, and two-thirds with Demeter."

Amazingly, all the gods agreed. Hades was happy to have his wife, even for just a third of the year. Demeter was overjoyed, though she never got over being mad at Hades. Whenever Persephone was in the Underworld, Demeter turned cold and angry and wouldn't let the plants grow.

According to the old stories, that's why there are three distinct seasons in Greece, and during the colder months of autumn, crops don't grow.

As for Persephone, the whole experience kind of forced her to grow up. She fell in love with Hades and made a place for herself in the Underworld, though she still enjoyed spending time in the mortal world with her mom and her old friends. The magic Titan Hecate, who had helped Demeter search, went to the Underworld and became one of Persephone's attendants. That was cool with Hecate. The Underworld was much darker, and a better place to work magic than a drafty cave.

Demeter even remembered her promise to Triptolemus, the prince of Eleusis. She gave him his own serpent-wheeled chariot and made him the god of farming. She told him to travel the world and teach people about agriculture. It doesn't sound like a very flashy job, but I guess Triptolemus liked it better than being thrown in a bed of fire.

After that, Demeter really *did* settle down. She didn't throw any more tantrums, which was good, because once her sister Hera got started, Hera's temper would make Demeter's anger look *tame*.

HERA GETS A
LITTLE CUCKOO

Let's start with the good news. Hera was hot. I
mean totally knockout gorgeous.

She had long licorice-black hair. Her face was regal
and unapproachably beautiful, like the face of a supermodel on
a fashion runway. The Greeks described her eyes as "oxlike."
Believe it or not, that was a compliment. It meant she had large,
soft brown eyes that you could get lost in. I guess the Greeks
spent a lot of time staring at oxen.

Anyway, in the early days of Mount Olympus, all the male
gods and Titans were falling over themselves for Hera. Which
brings us to the bad news. Hera had a short temper and massive
attitude. Whenever a guy approached her, she would cut him
down so fast—pointing out his faults, trash-talking him like
a pro—that the guy would leave in tears and never try flirting
with her again.

Mother Rhea decided Hera would do well at a boarding school for girls, where she could grow up a little and learn to be less abrasive. Unfortunately, nobody had invented boarding schools for girls yet.

Rhea did the next best thing. She sent Hera off to live with her Uncle Oceanus and Aunt Tethys at the bottom of the farthest sea.

For a while, Hera was off the radar screen. She spent some happy years with Oceanus and Tethys, who had a pretty solid marriage compared to the other immortals. Hera decided she wanted a marriage like that. She would hold out for the right guy. She wouldn't marry just any old god who came along, unless he could prove he would be a good and faithful husband.

She'd heard about her sister Demeter's troubles. Poseidon, Zeus, and Hades were all complete jerks. Hestia had been smart to stay single.

Hera wasn't about to be a bachelorette forever, though. She wanted a husband, kids, a house in the suburbs—the whole package. She would just have to be careful about *which* husband she chose.

After a few years, she moved back to Mount Olympus and got her own set of apartments in the palace. Her nasty temper was more under control, but the guy gods still found her hard to flirt with. If they got too fresh, she would shut them down *fast*.

Kiss Hera? I don't think so, loser. Not unless you show her a wedding ring and a financial statement proving you can support a family.

Eventually most of the gods and Titans decided Hera was

too much work, even though she was absolutely the most beautiful goddess in creation. (Well, so far, anyway.)

One god saw her as a challenge, though.

Zeus didn't like to take no for an answer. You may have noticed that.

He would slide in next to her at the dinner table and tell his best jokes. He would sing for her at the hearth. He would see her walking down the hall, and he'd suddenly bust into a Kouretes dance number just to get her to smile.

Secretly she enjoyed the attention. Zeus was funny when he wanted to be. He was handsome with his dark hair and blue eyes, and he liked to walk around without his shirt on, casually flexing his muscles and showing off his abs. He was in good shape, no doubt about it. And, yes, he was the king of the universe, so most women might consider him a good match.

But not Hera. She knew all about Zeus's womanizing. He'd already been married *at least* twice. He'd had a child with Demeter. There were rumors of many other affairs with goddesses, Titans, and even mortals.

Hera was *not* going to be another conquest. She wasn't a trophy. She knew that if she ever gave in to Zeus, he would lose interest in her immediately, stop being so charming, and go off to flirt with other women. Hera couldn't stand that idea.

One night at dinner he told a particularly funny joke— something about a donkey, a god, and a Cyclops walking into a temple—and Hera couldn't help laughing. She had tears in her eyes and couldn't breathe.

She gazed across the table and met Zeus's gaze a moment too long. She cleared her throat and looked away, but Zeus had glimpsed her feelings.

"You like me," he said. "You know you do."

"I certainly do *not*," she said. "You're a fool, a womanizer, a villain, and a liar!"

"Exactly!" Zeus said. "Those are my best qualities!"

She tried hard not to laugh. She'd never met a guy who was so immune to her insults. Zeus was almost as stubborn as she was.

"When will you give up?" she demanded. "I'm *not* interested."

"I'll never give up," he said. "And you *are* interested. You and I . . . king and queen of the cosmos. Imagine it! We'd be an unbeatable couple. Clearly, you are the most beautiful goddess in creation. And I, of course, am devilishly handsome."

He flexed his muscles. He was a ridiculous show-off, but Hera had to admit he was buff.

She shook her head. "How can I convince you that you're wasting your time?"

"You can't. I love you."

She snorted. "You love anything in a dress."

"This is different. You're the right goddess. I know it. You do, too. Just say *I love you*. You can do it. You'll feel better if you're honest."

"Never," she said. "I will never tell you that. *Ever.*"

"Oh, sounds like a challenge!" Zeus grinned. "If I can get you to admit you love me, will you marry me?"

Hera rolled her eyes. "Sure, Zeus. Since that will never happen, I can safely say that if I ever admitted to . . . you know, what you said . . . then sure, I'd marry you. Which I can only promise because IT WILL NEVER HAPPEN!"

Zeus winked. "Challenge accepted."

He left the dinner table, and Hera began wondering if she'd somehow made a mistake.

By a few nights later, Hera had almost forgotten about the conversation. Strangely, Zeus hadn't mentioned it again. In fact, he hadn't paid much attention to her at all since that night—which should have filled her with relief, but somehow it bummed her out.

Forget him, she told herself. *He finally got the message. He's probably accosting some other poor goddess.*

She tried to convince herself this was good news. She wasn't jealous. That would be ridiculous.

During the night, a huge thunderstorm raged over Mount Olympus—which probably should've made Hera suspicious, since Zeus was the god of the sky, and all—but she was too busy covering her windows to keep out the rain.

She ran to her bedroom and was just closing the last shutters when a small bird fluttered in and collapsed, exhausted, on her floor.

"Yikes!" Hera stepped back in alarm. "How did *you* get here?"

The bird flapped helplessly on the marble tiles. Its chest heaved, its whole body shivering from the cold. Hera knelt down and saw that it was a cuckoo.

Have you ever seen an *actual* cuckoo bird (not the carved ones that pop out of old clocks)? I haven't. I had to look it up. It's a weird-looking little guy. It's got a sort of Mohawk thing going on with its head feathers, which don't match its sleek brown-and-white wings or its long tail. Basically, it looks like its head got zapped in some mad scientist's device, so I can see why *cuckoo* became another word for *crazy*.

Anyway, Hera knelt down and scooped up the bird. She could feel its heart beating against her palm. One of its wings was bent the wrong way. Hera didn't understand how such a small bird could have flown all the way up to Mount Olympus. Usually only eagles flew that high, since the airspace around Olympus was restricted.

On the other hand, Hera knew that storms had powerful winds. Possibly the poor bird just got swept away.

"It's a miracle you're alive," Hera told the bird. "Don't worry, little guy. I'll take care of you."

She made a nest of blankets at the foot of her bed and gently set the bird inside. She dried its wings and fed it a few drops of nectar, which seemed to help. The cuckoo puffed up its feathers. It closed its eyes and started to make whistling, snoring noises, like soft notes played on a flute. Hera found the sound pleasing.

"I'll just keep him overnight," she said to herself. (She'd decided it was a boy.) "If he's better in the morning, I'll send him on his way."

In the morning, the cuckoo made no attempt to fly away. He sat contentedly on Hera's finger, eating pieces of seed and nut out of her hand. Hera had never had a pet before, and it made her smile.

"You're a good friend, aren't you?" she murmured to the bird.

"Coo," said the cuckoo.

Hera's heart warmed as she looked into his trusting orange eyes. "Should I keep you?"

"Coo." The cuckoo rubbed his beak on her finger in an unmistakably affectionate way.

Hera laughed in delight. "All right, then. Yes. I love you, too."

Instantly the cuckoo hopped to the floor. It began to grow. At first Hera was afraid she'd fed him too much nectar and the bird was going to explode, which would have been both distressing and messy. Instead, the bird took on the form of a god. Suddenly Zeus was standing before her in his glowing white robes, his golden crown gleaming in his black hair, which was still mussed up in a cuckoo-style hairdo.

"Sweet words, my lady," Zeus said. "*I love you, too.* Now, I believe you and I had a deal."

Hera was so stunned, she couldn't respond. Anger overwhelmed her. But she also felt a creeping admiration for what an incredible no-good scoundrel Zeus was. She wasn't sure whether she should hit him or laugh at him or just kiss him. He *was* awfully cute.

"On one condition," she said tightly.

"Name it."

"If I marry you," she said, "you will be a good, *faithful* husband. No more playing around. No more affairs or chasing after pretty mortals. I will not be made a laughingstock."

Zeus counted on his fingers. "That seems like more than one condition. But never mind! I accept!"

Hera should have made him promise on the River Styx, which is the most serious oath the gods can make. She didn't, though. She agreed to marry him.

After that, the cuckoo became one of her sacred animals. You'll usually see pictures of Hera holding a staff topped with either a cuckoo or a lotus flower, which was her sacred plant. In case you're curious, her other sacred animal was the cow, because it was such a motherly animal. Personally, if somebody told me, "Wow, babe, you remind me of a heifer," I would not take it as a compliment; but it didn't seem to bother Hera. Whatever clunks your cowbell, I suppose.

Zeus and Hera announced the happy news, and the gods began preparing for the biggest wedding in the history of weddings.

You have to pity Hermes the messenger god, who had to deliver the wedding invitations. Every god, Titan, mortal, nymph, satyr, and animal in the world was invited to join the party. I hope the snails got their invites early. It must've taken them forever to get there.

Different people will tell you different stories about where the wedding was held. We'll go with the island of Crete, because it makes sense. That was where Zeus hid on Mount Ida when he was a baby, so the place had good karma.

I'm still trying to figure out the logistics, though. . . . So, you invite a wild rabbit living in Italy to a party on the island of Crete. What's it supposed to do, swim there? Its little tux would get wet.

Anyway, everybody who was invited showed up, except for one really stupid nymph named Chelone. She lived in Arcadia on the Greek mainland, in this hut by a river, and she just threw her invitation away.

"Meh," she said. "Stupid wedding. I'd rather stay home."

When Hermes discovered she was a no-show, he got mad.

(I guess it was also his job to check the guest list.) He flew back to Chelone's place and found her bathing in the river.

"What's the deal?" he demanded. "You're not even dressed. The wedding is on!"

"Uh . . ." Chelone said. "I, um . . . I'm a little slow. I'll be there!"

"Really? That's the story you're going with?"

"Okay, no," she admitted. "I just wanted to stay home."

Hermes got a dark look in his eyes. "Fine."

He marched over to Chelone's hut and picked up the entire building, Superman-style. "You want to stay home? Stay home *forever*."

He threw the house right on top of her, but instead of dying, Chelone changed form. The house shrank over her back, melting into a shell, and Chelone became the world's first tortoise, an animal that's always slow and carries its house on its back. That's why *chelone* means *tortoise* in Greek. Hey, you never know. You might need that info on *Jeopardy!* someday.

The rest of the world was smart and went to the party. The bride and groom entered the sacred grove in a golden chariot driven by Eos, the Titan of the dawn, so rosy red light spread over the crowd as Zeus and Hera approached, signaling the dawning of a new day. The Three Fates officiated at the ceremony, which would have made me nervous. Those creepy old ladies could control the future and snip your lifeline, so you'd have to take your vows pretty seriously.

Hera and Zeus became man and wife, king and queen of the universe.

Everybody gave them amazing presents, but the last one

was Hera's favorite. The earth rumbled, and a sapling burst from the ground—a young apple tree bearing solid gold fruit. There was no card attached, but Hera knew it was a gift from her grandmother Gaea, who was still asleep, but who must have sensed a party going on.

Hera ordered the apple tree taken to the farthest western corner of the earth, where it was replanted in a beautiful garden right at the feet of the Titan Atlas, who was still holding up the sky. She sent an immortal dragon named Ladon to guard the tree, along with a group of Atlas's daughters called the Hesperides, the nymphs of the evening sky.

Why Hera planted her apple tree way out there instead of keeping it on Mount Olympus, I don't know. Maybe she just wanted to make it harder for heroes to steal her apples later on. If so, her plan worked . . . mostly.

Zeus and Hera stayed happily married for three hundred years, which isn't a long time for gods but is better than your average Hollywood marriage. They had three kids together: a boy, Ares, who was what you'd call a problem child; a girl, Hebe, who became the goddess of eternal youth; and another girl, Eileithyia, who became the goddess of childbirth. Kind of bad planning—having the goddess of childbirth *last*, after you've had two kids. It's almost like Hera thought, Wow, this child-bearing stuff? This hurts! We should have a goddess for this.

After their third kid was born, Zeus started to get the four-hundred-year itch. He remembered the good old days when he was a single guy, ambushing goddesses in snake pits and fun stuff like that. He started looking at other women and flirting again.

He'd promised to be a good husband, and he *had* been . . . for a while. But when you're immortal, those vows about "as long as you both shall live" take on a whole new meaning.

The more he flirted, the more upset and suspicious Hera got.

What she hated most were all the kids Zeus had by other women. They just kept popping up like weeds. Zeus claimed they were all from previous relationships, but that excuse didn't really cut it. Some of these kids were mortal, and they definitely didn't look over three hundred years old. Every time one of them showed up, Hera imagined the other gods snickering behind her back, whispering about what a fool she'd been to trust Zeus.

Finally she blew her lid.

She shouted at Zeus, "You keep having kids without me! You think that's funny? You think I appreciate your going back on your promise?"

Zeus frowned. "Is that a trick question?"

"See how you like it!" Hera cried. "I'm going to have a kid without you, without *any* man! I'll have a baby all by myself!"

Zeus scratched his head. "Uh, honey, I don't think it works that way."

"Bah!" Hera marched out of the throne room.

I don't know how she did it. Since her wedding with Zeus, Hera had become the goddess of marriage and motherhood, so I suppose she had certain powers. Anyway, out of sheer force of will, some very effective breathing exercises, possibly some Eastern meditation, and a proper diet, Hera got pregnant magically, with absolutely no help.

That was the good news.

The bad news? When the baby arrived, he looked like he could've *used* some help. His head was misshapen. His whole body was covered with patches of curly black hair. He had a large chest and bulky arms, but his legs were shriveled and bent, one slightly longer than the other. Instead of crying, he made grunting noises like he really needed to use the bathroom.

He was the ugliest kid Hera had ever seen. Even though he was her own baby, she felt no motherly connection at all—no love, just embarrassment.

Personally, I'm not surprised things turned out badly. I mean, you have a baby for revenge? That's a pretty messed-up reason, but it wasn't the kid's fault.

Hera said to herself: *I can't show this baby to the other gods. I'll be ridiculed.* She went to the open window of her bedroom and looked down the side of Mount Olympus. It sure was a long way down.

Who would ever know if the kid disappeared? She could always claim that she'd never been pregnant. False alarm.

Before she could rethink this pretty terrible idea, she tossed the baby out the window.

I know. *Totally* cold. Like a kid is something you can just throw away. But Hera was complicated that way. One day she was the perfect mother. The next day she was throwing babies out the window.

Oh, but the kid wasn't gone. His name was Hephaestus, and we'll see what happened to him later on.

In the meantime, Hera had other problems to deal with.

The first time a mortal hero visited Mount Olympus, it was a big deal. His name was Ixion, and apparently he was the first human to figure out that you could kill other humans in battle. *Congratulations! You win a prize!*

The gods were so impressed that he'd learned to fight other humans with an actual sword instead of just chucking rocks and grunting at them, they invited Ixion to a feast on Mount Olympus.

You'd think the guy would be on his best behavior. Nope.

He had too much to eat and drink. All the praise went to his head. He started thinking the gods were actually his friends, his peers, his comrades. Big mistake. No matter how nicely the gods treat you, they *never* see you as their equal. Remember, to them we are gerbils who have fire, cockroaches who can use weapons. We're kind of entertaining. Occasionally we're useful, if the gods need to kill small things down on earth. But BFFs? No.

All evening, Ixion kept making eyes at Hera, since she was the most beautiful lady at the table. Zeus was too busy partying to notice, much less care. Finally Hera got really uncomfortable and excused herself.

Ixion figured that was his cue to follow her. The guy had learned how to kill people, but apparently he had a lot to learn about goddesses. After she'd left, Ixion waited at the table for a few minutes, then he announced to the gods, "Hey, all this drink is going right through me. Where's the bathroom? Uh, do gods even *have* bathrooms?"

"Down the hall," Zeus said. "First door on the right. They're marked *mortals* and *gods*. Just be sure you use the correct one."

Ixion headed off in the direction Hera had gone. He found her standing on a balcony, looking at the clouds.

"Hey, beautiful," he said.

She flinched. She probably would have turned him into some form of snail—something very slimy—but she was too stunned that this mortal had dared to speak to her.

Ixion took her silence as shyness. "Yeah, I know you've been checking me out. I think you're awesome, too. How about a kiss?"

He put his arm around her and tried to kiss her. Hera was so panicked, all she could do was push him away and run. She lost him in the corridors of the palace, locked herself in her room, and waited until her pulse returned to normal.

Why hadn't she incinerated him? Or at least changed him into a slug?

She'd been too shocked. Also, maybe, she was a little confused by the flirting. It had been several hundred years since she'd had to deal with that. Once she'd gotten married, she'd put other men out of her mind completely.

Whatever Hera's faults, she was *not* a cheater. She didn't have an unfaithful bone in her immortal body. She truly and honestly believed that marriage was forever, for better or worse, which was why Zeus's little adventures drove her into a rage.

Once she had calmed down, she started to plot her revenge. She could punish Ixion herself, sure. But why not tell Zeus instead? Let *him* be the jealous one for a change. Maybe if he had to defend her honor, he would start taking his marriage vows more seriously.

Hera composed herself and returned to the dinner table. Ixion sat there chatting away, as if nothing had happened—the little weasel. Hera gave him a smile, just to show she wasn't rattled. Then she leaned over to Zeus and whispered, "My lord, may I speak with you in private?"

Zeus frowned. "Am I in trouble?"

"Not yet," she said sweetly.

She led him down the hall and explained what had happened.

Zeus scowled. He stroked his beard thoughtfully.

Hera had been hoping he would march right back into the dining room and blast Ixion to ashes, but he didn't.

"Did you *hear* me?" Hera asked. "Why aren't you getting angry?"

"Oh, I heard you." Zeus cleared his throat. "It's just . . . well, he's a guest in my house. He's eaten our food. I can't incinerate him without good reason."

"WITHOUT GOOD REASON?" she cried. "He made a pass at your *wife!"*

"Yes, yes. And that's very serious. Still, I need indisputable proof."

"My word is not good enough?" Hera was about to throw Zeus off the balcony and take care of Ixion herself, but Zeus raised his hands to placate her.

"I have a plan," he said. "We'll see if Ixion really intended to dishonor you, or if he just made a drunken, stupid mistake. Once we have proof, none of the other gods will object to my punishing this mortal, even though he is my guest. Trust me. If he's guilty, his punishment will be spectacular."

Hera clenched her fists. "Do what you have to do."

Zeus reached over the railing and summoned down a cloud. It condensed and churned before him in a small white tornado, shaping itself into a humanoid figure. It became an exact replica of Hera, only pale and cold.

I take that back. It was an exact replica of Hera.

Fake Hera looked at Real Hera. "Hello."

"That is creepy," said Real Hera.

"Just wait here," Zeus told Real Hera.

He took Fake Hera back to the party.

Ixion picked up right where he'd left off, flirting with Fake Hera. To his delight, Fake Hera flirted back. She gestured for him to follow her down the hall. One thing led to another.

In the morning, the bleary-eyed gods stumbled into the dining hall for breakfast. They were surprised to find that Ixion had stayed overnight, and when they asked why, Ixion told them that the Queen of Heaven had invited him to stay in her apartment—wink, wink, wink.

"I have her wrapped around my little finger," he bragged. "She said I was *much* handsomer than Zeus. She's going to make me immortal just so she can be with me forever."

He went on boasting about how cool he was and how much Hera wanted to leave Zeus and marry him. Meanwhile, Zeus himself entered the dining hall and walked up quietly behind Ixion.

Finally Ixion realized that all the gods at the table had gone silent.

He faltered. "He's right behind me, isn't he?"

"Why, yes!" Zeus said cheerfully. "And if you're going to steal another man's wife, you really shouldn't brag about it in his own house. Also, you should make sure it's *actually* the man's wife you stole, and not a cloud dummy."

Ixion gulped. "I guess I'm in trouble."

"Just a bit!" Zeus agreed.

None of the other gods objected to Zeus's punishing his guest. Zeus called for a spare chariot wheel and strapped Ixion to the spokes, stretching his limbs so tight, they were about to snap. Then he set the wheel on fire and threw it into the sky like a Frisbee. Ixion became immortal, all right, but only so he could suffer eternal agony. He's still up there in orbit, spinning and burning and screaming, "Hera! I thought you liked me!"

The strangest part of the story? Fake Hera actually had a baby. How does a cloud have a baby? I have no clue, but their son was a guy named Centaurus, who apparently fell in love with a horse—again, no clue. Their kids became the race of centaurs, who are half human, half horse.

Like I told you at the beginning, I couldn't make up stuff this weird.

Hera hoped Zeus would be a more attentive husband after the Ixion incident, but she was disappointed. Instead, Zeus seemed to think he'd successfully defended Hera's honor, so now he deserved some playtime.

If I tried to tell you all the times Hera took revenge on Zeus's girlfriends, we'd be here for a century. It sort of became Hera's full-time job.

But one particular mortal girl *really* got under her skin. Semele was a princess of the Greek city of Thebes, and though no one dared to say it aloud, everyone knew she was the most beautiful mortal of her generation—as beautiful as a goddess, perhaps even more beautiful than Hera herself.

Zeus started taking a lot of "shopping trips" down to Thebes. Hera was suspicious, of course, but Zeus was clever.

Hera could never catch him and Semele together. Then one day she was hovering over Thebes as a golden cloud when she happened to spot Zeus (in disguise as a mortal, but Hera could still recognize him) exiting a house in the best part of town.

A moment later, Semele appeared at the door and waved after him. The girl only stood there for a second, but one thing was obvious: she was *immensely* pregnant.

Hera snarled and muttered to herself, but she couldn't simply kill the girl outright. Even though Zeus was a no-good scumbag, he was a very *powerful* no-good scumbag. If he found out that Hera had killed one of his girlfriends, he could inflict all sorts of pain and suffering on her. She would have to work through trickery.

Hera floated down to Thebes in her golden cloud and took the form of an old woman. She knocked on Semele's door, thinking she would pretend to be a beggar or perhaps a traveling saleslady.

Semele opened the door and gasped. "Beroe, is that you?"

Hera had no idea what the girl was talking about, but she played along. "Why, yes, my dear! It is I, Beroe, your, um—"

"My nursemaid from childhood!"

"Exactly!"

"Oh, you have aged so!"

"Thanks," Hera muttered.

"But I would still know you anywhere. Please, come in!"

Hera got a tour of the house. She was outraged to find it was just as nice, if not better, than her own apartment on Mount Olympus.

She asked innocently how Semele came by such an amazing mansion, which seemed elaborate even for a princess.

"Oh, it's my boyfriend," Semele said, beaming with pride. "He's so awesome, he gives me *anything* I want. Look at this necklace he just brought me."

She showed Hera a jade, gold, and ruby pendant that was much nicer than anything Zeus had ever given Hera.

"How lovely." Hera resisted the urge to punch the princess in her perfect teeth. "So, who is this guy? Is he local?"

"Oh . . . I'm not supposed to say."

"But I'm your old nursemaid, Beryl!" Hera said.

"Beroe," Semele said.

"That's what I meant! Surely you can tell me."

Semele was bursting with excitement. She'd been dying to tell someone, so she didn't take much convincing.

"Well . . . it's Zeus," she confessed. "The lord of the sky. The king of creation."

Hera stared at her, feigning disbelief. Then she sighed in sympathy. "Oh, my poor girl. My poor, poor girl."

Semele blinked. That wasn't the reaction she'd been expecting. "But . . . I'm dating the king of the universe!"

Hera snorted. "So he says. How many guys have used *that* line before? Like, every one of them! How do you know he's *actually* a god, and not just some rich old creep *pretending* to be a god?"

Semele's face reddened. "But he *said* he was Zeus. And he seems very . . . godly."

"Has he done anything to prove it?"

"Uh, well, no."

Hera pretended to think about the problem. "This is the father of your child. You should be sure. You said he would do anything for you?"

"Yes! He promised!"

"Get him to swear," Hera advised. "Then ask him to appear before you the way he appears before his wife Hera—in his true godly form. That's the only way you'll know for sure."

Semele pondered this. "Sounds dangerous."

"Not if he truly loves you! Are you not as good as Hera?"

"Of course."

"And as beautiful?"

"More beautiful. Zeus told me so."

Hera clenched her jaw so hard, she cracked an immortal tooth. "There you go, then. If Hera can handle Zeus's godly form, then surely you can too! I hope he really is Zeus, my dear. Honestly! But you must be sure. Your child's future is on the line. When is he coming back?"

"Very soon, actually."

"Well, look at the time!" Hera said. "Wonderful catching up, but I should go. I have . . . old-lady things to do."

Hera left. An hour later, Zeus returned to Semele's house.

"Hey, babe," he said as he walked in.

Immediately he noticed something was wrong. Semele didn't run up and hug him and kiss him as usual. She was sulking on her couch with her arms crossed across her pregnant belly.

"Uh . . . what's up?" Zeus asked.

Semele pouted. "You said you'd do anything for me."

"And I will! You want another necklace?"

"No," she said. "I want a different favor. Only one thing will make me happy."

Zeus chuckled. Maybe Semele wanted a dress this time, or a pair of those new things the humans had just invented . . . what were they called . . . shoes?

"Anything you want," Zeus said.

"Promise?"

He spread his arms magnanimously. "I swear on the River Styx. Ask me any favor, and it's yours."

"Good." She allowed herself a smile. "I want you to appear before me in your true godly form, the way you appear to Hera."

Zeus sucked in his breath. "Oh . . . bad idea, babe. Ask me something else."

"No!" Semele struggled to her feet. "You said *anything*. I want proof that you're really a god. I'm just as good as Hera! I want to see you the way *she* sees you."

"But a god's true form . . . that's not for mortals to look on. Especially pregnant mortals. Especially pregnant mortals who would like to live longer than a few seconds."

"I can handle it," she said. "I *know* I can."

Zeus was not so sure about that. He'd never actually tried appearing to a mortal in his pure godly form before, but he imagined that for the mortal, it would be like looking at the sun without protective eyewear, or looking at an actor first thing in the morning pre-makeup. *Dangerous.*

On the other hand, Zeus had sworn on the River Styx, and he couldn't back out of that. Also, Semele was a feisty girl. She was the daughter of the famous hero Cadmus. If she thought she could handle seeing a god's true form, maybe she could.

"Okay, ready?" Zeus asked.

"Ready."

Zeus's mortal disguise burned away. He appeared in all his glory as a swirling pillar of fire and lightning, like a supernova, in Semele's living room. The furniture went up in flames. The door blew off its hinges. The window shutters exploded.

Semele couldn't handle it. She vaporized, leaving an after-image scorch mark on the living room wall. However, the baby inside her *did* survive, probably because he was part god. The poor little guy was suddenly hovering in midair where his nice cozy mother used to be. Zeus took physical form just in time to catch him before he hit the floor.

Of course Zeus was in shock over Semele's death, but he realized that the most important thing right now was the baby. The little dude wasn't fully grown yet. He obviously needed a few more months to develop before he was ready to be born.

Zeus had to think quickly. He pulled out his lightning bolt and made an incision in his own right thigh. Must've hurt like crazy, but Zeus stuffed the baby into his thigh just like he was putting him in the pocket of a pair of cargo pants. Then he sewed his skin shut.

Guys . . . do not try this at home. It won't work.

But I guess gods are different. Somehow the kid stayed alive in there and kept growing until he was ready to be born.

No word on whether the other gods said, "Hey, Zeus, why is your right thigh so huge, dude? You should really get that looked at."

When the baby was ready, Zeus cut him out; and the kid became the god Dionysus. We'll get to his story later on. His birth is the *least* strange thing about him.

Anyway, Hera got her revenge on Semele, and I wish I could tell you it was the harshest thing she ever did.

Unfortunately, she was just getting warmed up.

Another one of Zeus's girlfriends was this lady named Aigina. Apparently, Aigina had heard the story about Semele, because she was not anxious to become Zeus's special friend, even though he constantly flirted with her and showered her with gifts. Finally, Zeus convinced her to fly away with him to a secret island.

"No one will ever know," he promised.

"What about Hera?" Aigina asked.

"Especially not her." Zeus turned into a giant eagle and flew her to an island that now bears her name: Aigina.

Zeus *almost* got away with it. Hera didn't find out about the affair until years later, after Aigina had passed away. By then, Aigina and Zeus's son was the king of the island where he'd been born. I don't know how Hera found out, but once she did, she was outraged that she couldn't punish Aigina personally.

"How *dare* she die so that I can't kill her!" Hera growled. "Well, I'll just take out my anger on her son."

His name was King Aeacus (I think he needs a few more vowels in his name. No idea how to pronounce it, so I'm going with *Eye-AH-cuss*.) Anyway, King Aeacus happened to be on the verge of war. He was getting his armies together to defend his kingdom.

Hera summoned a massive poisonous snake and dropped it into the headwaters of the island's only river. The venom spread through the water supply, and soon most of the population of the entire island was dead.

Hey, that's fair, right? Zeus sleeps with a mortal woman, so Hera finds the woman's son and kills everyone in his kingdom. No, that's not psychotic at all.

As you can imagine, Aeacus panicked. He went to his palace garden, where he could see the blue sky. He fell on his knees and prayed to Zeus, "Hey, Dad, I'm about to get invaded here, and your wife just pretty much killed every man in my army and most of the civilians."

Zeus's voice rumbled from the heavens: "Bummer. How can I help?"

Aeacus thought about that. He looked down at his flower-beds and saw ants marching around, thousands of the little dudes, tireless and industrious like . . . like an army.

"You know what would be cool?" Aeacus asked. "If you could turn these ants into an army for me."

"Done!" Zeus thundered.

Immediately the entire colony of ants grew into men—thousands of hardened warriors in gleaming red-and-black armor, already drilled to march in rows and fight with perfect discipline. They feared no enemy. They were incredibly strong and tough. They were called the Myrmidones, and they became the most famous elite fighting unit in Greece, like the Navy SEALs or the Green Berets of the ancient world. Later on, they would have a famous commander named Achilles. Maybe you've heard of him, or at least his heel.

The last thing about Hera—and I really don't get this—is how quickly she could change from being somebody's enemy to his friend, or vice versa. Take Poseidon, for instance.

At first, they didn't get along. In fact, they both had their eye on the same Greek kingdom, called Argos. See, it was a big deal back then to be the patron god of this city or that city. Like, it was a huge honor if you could claim to be the god of New York City. If you were the god of Scranton, Pennsylvania . . . not so much. (Okay, sorry, everybody in Scranton. But you get the idea.)

I guess Argos was a nice place, because both Hera and Poseidon wanted to be its patron. The king decided to go for Hera. Probably he didn't want his population dying off from snake poison.

Hera was delighted. Poseidon wasn't. He flooded the entire kingdom, and when Hera complained, Poseidon said, "Fine. I'll take back the water. I'll take back *all* of it." The sea receded, and all the springs and rivers in the whole country went dry.

Hera complained again. The two of them were on the verge of an epic smackdown. Finally Poseidon relented and let some of the water come back, but Argos is still a very dry place. Many of the rivers have no water unless it rains. Hera became the patron of Argos, which was helpful later on for a dude named Jason, who led a crew of heroes called the Argonauts. But that's another story.

My point is that Hera changed her tune shortly afterward. She and Poseidon had a sit-down and decided that Zeus was getting out of control as a leader. They plotted the first-ever Olympian rebellion.

But we'll get to that when we talk about Poseidon.

Now we have to visit the Underworld and see how it's going with our favorite creepy stalker death god, Hades.

HADES DOES HOME IMPROVEMENT

I FEEL FOR THE GUY.

No, seriously.

Hades might be a creep, but there's no doubt he got the short end of the universe. Despite being Rhea's oldest son, he was always counted as the youngest, since the gods went by the order they got barfed from Kronos's gut.

If that wasn't bad enough, when the gods rolled dice to divide up the world, Hades got the least desirable part—the Underworld.

Of course, Hades was kind of a gloomy dude to begin with, so you could argue that he was destined to hang out underground. He was always brooding and dressed in black. His dark hair covered his eyes like one of those emo dudes from Japanese manga. Once he became lord of the Underworld, all the color drained out of his complexion, because he was leaving the mortal world behind.

Even if the other gods *wanted* to keep in touch with him (which they didn't), the Underworld had really bad phone service and zero Wi-Fi. When Hades was down there, he had no idea what was going on in the world above. His only news came from the spirits of the recently dead, who would fill him in on the latest gossip.

In fact, in Ancient Greek times, whenever you invoked the name of Hades, you had to bang your fist against the ground, because that was the only way to get his attention. Kind of like, *Hey, I'm talking to you!*

Why would you *want* to get Hades's attention? I'm not sure.

Eventually the entire Underworld would be called *Hades* after the god Hades, which made things confusing; but the Underworld had actually been around much longer than the god. Its original name was Erebos, and when Hades took over, the place was a real fixer-upper.

Let's start with the plumbing. Five different rivers flowed into the Underworld, and you wouldn't want to use any of them for taking a bath or brushing your teeth. The *least* dangerous was the Cocytus, the River of Wailing, which looked tame enough. Its dark-blue waters wound peacefully through the plains of Erebos, with plenty of nice-looking spots on the riverbank for a picnic; but if you got too close, you would hear the cries of tortured souls churning in the current.

See, the Cocytus was fed by the tears of the damned. Just being near it would send you into a state of depression. If you actually *touched* the water . . . well, trust me, you didn't want to do that. No amount of cute puppy videos on the Internet would ever lift your spirits again.

The second river was the Phlegethon, the River of Fire. It roared through the Underworld caverns like a torrent of burning gasoline, cutting channels through the black volcanic rock, lighting everything bloodred, filling the air with smoke and fumes until finally the river plummeted as a fiery waterfall into the deeper abyss of Tartarus, which was like the basement of the basement.

So, yeah . . . when Hades turned on the hot water in his shower, he got a face full of burning Phlegethon. No wonder the guy was always in a bad mood.

The crazy thing was, Phlegethon water wouldn't kill you, even if you were mortal. Sure, it would burn like radioactive chili peppers sautéed in acid. It would make you *wish* you were dead. But the river was actually designed to keep its victims alive so that they could suffer forever—hooray! Many damned souls had to swim through it for all eternity, or be stuck in the fiery water up to their necks.

According to some legends, the Phlegethon could eventually burn away your sins and let you go free if you were really, really sorry for the things you'd done. If you want to test that theory, go ahead and jump in. Me, I think I'll pass.

River number three, the Acheron, was the River of Pain. If you guessed it was painful, you win a cookie! The Acheron started in the mortal world, near a temple of the dead in Epirus. Maybe that's why ghosts were drawn to it and filled the river with their own pain and suffering. The Acheron meandered along until it plunged underground and tumbled into Erebos. There it widened into a dark, steamy, swampy expanse that caused pain to anyone unlucky enough to touch its waters or even *hear* its current. After a while, the Acheron split into two smaller rivers—the Cocytus and the Styx—that flowed in opposite directions until they both spilled into Tartarus.

River number four was my least personal favorite: the Lethe, River of Forgetfulness. (I've had some bad experiences with amnesia. Long story.) Anyway, the Lethe looked harmless. In most places it was a gentle span of milky-white water that rolled over a shallow bed of stones, softly gurgling in a way that made your eyes feel heavy. You would think you could wade across this river, no problem. My advice? Don't.

A single drop of Lethe water would wipe your short-term memory. You wouldn't remember anything that happened in the last week. Take a full drink, or wade into those waters, and your mind would be completely erased. You wouldn't remember your own name, or where you came from, or even that the New York Yankees are *obviously* better than the Boston Red Sox. I know—terrifying, right?

For some spirits of the dead, however, the Lethe was actually a blessing. Crowds of ghosts were always gathered at the banks, drinking from the river so that they could forget their former lives, because you can't miss what you don't remember. Occasionally spirits were even allowed to reincarnate—to be reborn in the mortal world for another life. If you took that chance, you *had* to drink from the Lethe first so that you wouldn't remember your old life. Because, seriously—who would want to go through twelve boring years of school again if you remembered doing it before?

Poppies grew all along the banks of the Lethe, which is why poppy juice has the power to put people to sleep and dull their pain. (We call that *opium*, children. And don't do drugs, because DRUGS ARE BAD. Okay, I had to put that in there.) At one point, the Lethe curved around the entrance of a dark cave where the god Hypnos lived—the god of sleep. What was it like inside? No one has ever described it, probably because anyone stupid enough to go in fell asleep and never came out again.

The fifth river of the Underworld was the Styx, the River of Hate. It was definitely the most famous river, but the name alone sort of dampened any chance for tourism. *"Hey, kids, we're going to the River of Hate for spring break!"* *"Yay!"*

The Styx flowed through the deepest, darkest parts of the Underworld. Some legends claimed it was created by the water Titan, Tethys, and was fed by salty springs from the bottom of the ocean.

The Styx circled Erebos like a moat, so you pretty much *had* to cross it to get into the Underworld. (Some stories say the Acheron was the river you had to cross, but since the Styx was a branch of the Acheron, I guess both versions are correct.)

The current was dark and sluggish, always shrouded in foul-smelling mist, and the water was corrosive to mortal flesh. Mix sulfuric acid with sewage and a splash of liquid hatred, and you've got the Styx.

So you're wondering: Why would anybody *want* to get into the Underworld? I don't know. But ever since humans were created, whenever they died, their souls just sort of instinctively drifted down to Erebos, like lemmings jumping off a cliff, or tourists flocking to Times Square. You could tell them all you wanted that it was a stupid idea, but they just kept doing it.

The problem was, the souls had no reliable way to cross the River Styx. A few managed to swim it. Others tried, only to dissolve in the water. Many just wandered along the mortal side of the river, wailing and pointing at the other side like, *I wanna go that way!*

Finally, one industrious daimon named Charon decided to go into business. What's a daimon? It's not a devil-type demon with a pitchfork and a tail and red skin. Daimons were immortal spirits, kind of like lesser gods. Some looked like monsters or mortals. Some were good. Some were bad. Some just kind of hung around.

This dude Charon was a son of Nyx, the goddess of night. Charon could take different forms, but most of the time he appeared as an ugly old man in tattered robes, with a greasy beard and a cone-shaped hat. If it was me and I could change shape, I would walk around looking like Brad Pitt; but I guess Charon didn't care about impressing the ghosts.

At any rate, one day Charon realized that all these mortal souls were clamoring to get to Erebos, so Charon built himself a boat and started ferrying people across.

Not for free, of course. He accepted gold, silver, and most major credit cards. Since the Underworld had no regulations, Charon just charged whatever he wanted to. If he liked you, he might let you across for a couple of coins. If he didn't like you, he'd demand a fortune. If you were unlucky enough to be buried without any money—oh, well! You'd have to wander around on the mortal side of the Styx forever. Some of the dead even drifted back to the mortal world to haunt the living as ghosts.

Even if you got across the Styx, you'd find Erebos in

complete chaos. The ghosts were *supposed* to divide into different groups according to how good they'd been in their lives. If they were real scum suckers, they went to the Fields of Punishment to enjoy special torture for eternity. If they were good, they went to Elysium, which was like Paradise, Las Vegas, and Disneyland rolled into one. If the spirits hadn't been particularly good or bad in life but had just sort of existed (which was most people), they were forced to wander forever in the Fields of Asphodel, which wasn't a horrible place—just incredibly, mind-numbingly boring.

That's how spirits got sorted, in theory. Unfortunately, before Hades took over, nobody was policing the Underworld. It was kind of like a school day when all your teachers are sick and you have nothing but subs who don't know the rules, so naturally the kids take total advantage. Doomed souls from Punishment sneaked into Asphodel and no one stopped them. The spirits from Asphodel crashed the party in Elysium. And some really dumb but noble spirits bound for Elysium took a wrong turn, ended up in Punishment, and either couldn't get out or were too nice to complain about it.

To make matters worse, even the spirits who went where they were supposed to go didn't always deserve to be there, because before Hades took over, you were judged for the afterlife while you were still alive.

How did that system work? I have no idea. Apparently a panel of three living judges interviewed you right before you died and decided if you deserved the Fields of Punishment, Elysium, or Asphodel. Don't ask me how the judges knew you were about to die. Maybe they guessed. Maybe the gods told them. Maybe the judges just yelled at random people, "Hey, you! Get over here! It's your turn to croak!"

Anyway, the judges listened to your testimony and decided your eternal fate. Guess what happened. People lied. They bribed the judges. They showed up in their best clothes, smiled and flattered and acted nice so the judges would think they *were* nice. They brought in witnesses to say, "Oh, yeah. This guy lived a *totally* awesome life. He hardly ever tortured anybody." Stuff like that.

A lot of evil people managed to charm their way into Elysium, and a lot of good people who didn't kiss up to the judges landed in the Fields of Punishment.

You get the idea . . . the Underworld was a mess. When Hades took over, he looked around and said, "Nuh-uh! This ain't gonna work!"

So he went to Olympus and explained the situation to Zeus. Having to get Zeus's approval for what he planned to do kind of rankled Hades, but he knew he'd need to get the Big Guy's thumbs-up for any major changes to the afterlife, especially since humans were involved. The gods considered humans shared property.

Zeus listened and frowned thoughtfully. "So what do you propose?"

"Well," Hades said, "we could keep the panel of three judges, but—"

"The audience could vote!" Zeus guessed. "At the end of each season, the winning mortal could be crowned Elysian Idol!"

"Uh, no," Hades said. "Actually, I was thinking the judges could be spirits of the dead rather than living people. And each mortal soul would only be judged once it enters the Underworld."

"So . . . not a competition format? Hmm, too bad."

Hades tried to keep his cool. "See, if the judges are spirits under my control, they'll be impossible to influence. The souls who come before the court will be stripped of everything but their essence. They can't rely on good looks or fancy clothes. They can't bribe the judges or call character witnesses. All their good and bad deeds will be laid bare, because the judges can literally see right through them. Lying will be impossible."

"I like it," Zeus said. "Who will you pick for judges?"

"Probably three deceased mortals who were kings in the upper world," Hades said. "Kings are used to passing judgment."

"Good," Zeus agreed. "As long as the kings are all *my* sons. Agreed?"

Hades gritted his teeth. He didn't like his brother getting involved in everything, but since almost every Greek king was a son of Zeus, there would still be plenty of kings to choose from. "Agreed."

Zeus nodded. "How will you make sure the judgments are enforced, and the souls go where they're supposed to?"

Hades smiled coldly. "Oh, don't worry. I've got that covered."

When he got back to Erebos, Hades appointed three former kings, all demigod sons of Zeus, as his dead-celebrity judges: Minos, Aiakos, and Rhadamanthys.

Then he rounded up the three Furies—those spirits of vengeance who had been formed from the blood of Ouranos ages before. Hades hired them to be his enforcers, which was a good call, since nobody wanted to cross a demonic grandmother with bad breath and a whip.

Like most daimons, the Furies could take different shapes, but usually they appeared as ugly old ladies with long stringy hair, black tattered robes, and giant bat wings. Their fiery whips could cause excruciating pain to the living or the dead, and they could fly invisibly, so you never knew when they would swoop down on you.

Hades used them to keep the dead in line. Sometimes he let the Furies go nuts and design new tortures for the worst of the doomed souls. He could even send the Furies after living people if they committed a truly horrific crime—like killing a family member, desecrating a temple, or singing Journey songs on karaoke night.

Hades's next Underworld improvement: he made it a lot easier for spirits of the dead to find their way to Erebos. He convinced Hermes, the messenger god, to keep a lookout for lost souls on the mortal side of the Styx. If Hermes saw any ghosts who looked confused, he would steer them in the right direction and provide them with a handy full-color map, compliments of the Underworld Chamber of Commerce.

Once the souls of the dead made it to the River Styx, the daimon Charon would ferry them across for a standard fee of one silver coin. Hades had convinced him (read: *threatened* him) to charge everyone the same price.

Hades also spread the word to the mortals up above that they'd better take their funeral rites seriously, or they wouldn't be allowed into the Underworld. When you died, your family was supposed to make offerings to the gods. They had to give you a decent burial and place a coin under your tongue so you could pay Charon. If you didn't have a coin, you'd end up haunting the mortal world as a ghost forever, which was both pointless and boring.

How did Hades spread the word among the mortals? He had this army of black-winged nasties called *oneiroi*, or dream daimons, who visited mortals while they slept, delivering visions or nightmares.

Ever had one of those dreams where you wake up startled because you felt like you were falling? That's the *oneiroi* messing with you. They probably picked you up and dropped you, just to be mean. Next time it happens, smack your fist on the floor and yell, "Hades, tell your stupid daimons to knock it off!"

Another upgrade Hades made: he tightened security at the gates of Erebos. He went down to the Tartarus Humane Society and adopted the biggest, baddest dog you can imagine—a monster named Cerberus, who was sort of a cross between a pit bull, a rottweiler, and a rabid woolly mammoth. Cerberus had three heads, so if you were a mortal hero trying to sneak into Hades's realm, or a dead person trying to sneak out, you had three times the chance of getting spotted and devoured. In addition to razor-sharp fangs and claws, Cerberus supposedly had a mane made out of snakes and a serpent for a tail. I can't vouch for that. I only met Cerberus once. It was dark, and I was mostly focused on not whimpering or wetting my pants.

Anyway, once the departed spirits got inside the gates, they were sorted out by the three dead-celebrity judges and ushered to their proper places. Like I said earlier, most people hadn't really done much with their lives, good or bad, so they ended up in the Fields of Asphodel. There they existed as wispy shadows that could only chitter like bats and float around aimlessly, trying to remember who they were and what they were doing—sort of like teachers during first period, before they've had enough coffee.

If you had led a good life, you went to Elysium, which was about as nice as you could get in the dark Underworld. You got a mansion of your own, free food and drinks, and pretty much five-star service for whatever you needed. You could hang out with the other lucky good people and chill for eternity. If Elysium got boring, you could choose to drink from the River Lethe and be reborn in a new mortal life.

A few souls were *so* good, they managed to live three virtuous lives in a row. If that was you, you could retire to the Isles of the Blest, which were Caribbean-type private islands in a lake in the middle of Elysium. Not many people were that lucky or that virtuous. It was sort of like winning the Good Person Powerball Lottery.

If you'd lived an evil life, you got the special naughty treatment—boiling in oil forever, having your skin flayed, getting chased by hungry demons over a field of broken glass, or sliding down a giant razor blade into a pool of lemon juice. You know, the usual. Most of the punishments weren't very creative, but if you managed to *really* annoy Hades, he could always come up with new and interesting ways to torture your immortal soul.

A couple of examples?

Tantalus. That dude was *messed up*. He was a Greek king—a son of Zeus, no surprise—who got invited to share ambrosia and nectar on Mount Olympus with the gods. Big honor, right? But Tantalus got greedy.

"Wow," he said after dinner, patting his belly. "That's good stuff! Could I get a doggie bag to share with my friends back home?"

"Holy me!" Zeus swore. "Absolutely not! This ambrosia and nectar is rare and magical stuff. You can't go sharing it with just anybody."

"Oh . . ." Tantalus forced a smile. "Of course. I see how it is. Well . . . next time, dinner at my place, huh?"

Tantalus should've let it go. He should've remembered what happened to Prometheus when he tried to take stuff from the gods and share it with mortals. But Tantalus was angry. He felt insulted. The gods didn't trust him. They didn't want him to become famous as the mortal who brought ambrosia to earth.

The more he thought about it, the angrier he got. He invited the gods to a feast at *his* palace, but to get back at them, he decided he would serve them the most insulting meal he could think of. He just wasn't sure *what.*

He was standing in his kitchen, staring at the empty cooking pots, when his son Pelops walked in.

"What's for dinner, Dad?" Pelops asked.

Tantalus had never liked his son. I don't know why. Maybe Tantalus knew the kid would take over his kingdom someday. Greek kings were always paranoid about stuff like that. Anyway, Tantalus gave his son an evil smile and pulled out a butcher's knife. "Funny you should ask."

That night, the gods gathered at Tantalus's palace for dinner and got served a pot of yummy stew.

"What is this meat?" Demeter said, taking the first bite. "Tastes like chicken."

Tantalus had meant to wait until all the gods had eaten,

but he couldn't hold in the crazy giggles. "Oh . . . just a family recipe."

Zeus frowned and put down his spoon. "Tantalus . . . what have you done?"

Hera pushed her bowl away. "And where is your son Pelops?"

"Actually," Tantalus said, "that's him in the stew. Surprise, you idiots! Ha, ha! Ha, ha!"

Honestly, I don't know what he was expecting. Did he think the gods would chuckle and slap him on the back? *Oh, Tantalus, you old kidder. Good one!*

The Olympians were horrified. After all, they still had post-traumatic stress from getting swallowed by their father, Kronos. Zeus pulled out a lightning bolt, blasted Tantalus to ashes, and turned the king's soul over to Hades.

"Make a special punishment for this one," Zeus said. "Something involving food, please."

Hades was happy to oblige. He sank Tantalus up to his waist in a pool of fresh water, his feet stuck in the riverbed like in cement. Over Tantalus's head hung the branches of a magical tree that grew all sorts of luscious fragrant fruits.

Tantalus's punishment was just to stand there forever.

Well, he thought, this isn't so bad.

Then he got hungry. He tried to grab an apple, but the branches rose just out of reach. He tried for a mango. No luck. He tried jumping, but his feet were stuck. He tried pretending to be asleep so he could launch a surprise attack on the peaches. Again, no luck. Each time, Tantalus was *sure* he would score a piece of fruit, but he never could.

When he got thirsty, he scooped up water, but by the time

his hands reached his mouth, the water had magically evaporated, and his hands were completely dry. He bent down, hoping to gulp straight from the lake, but the entire surface of the water shrank away from him. No matter what he tried, he couldn't get a single drop. He just got hungrier and thirstier, even though food and water were so close—*tantalizingly* close, which is a word that comes from his name. Next time you want something really badly but it's just out of reach, you've been tantalized.

What's the moral of the story? I dunno. Maybe: *Don't chop up your son and feed him to your dinner guests.* Seems kind of obvious to me, but whatever.

Another guy who got a special punishment was Sisyphus. With a name like *Sissy-Fuss* you have to figure the guy had issues, but at least he didn't make his kids into stew. Sisyphus's problem was that he didn't want to die.

I can relate to that. I wake up every morning and think: *You know what would be good today? Not dying.*

But Sisyphus took things too far. One day, Death showed up at his house. And by Death, I mean Thanatos, the god of death, the Grim Reaperino, who was one of Hades's main lieutenants.

Sisyphus opened the door and found a big guy with black feathery wings looming over him.

"Good afternoon." Thanatos consulted his notepad. "I have a delivery for Sisyphus—one painful death, requires a signature. Are you Sisyphus?"

Sisyphus tried to hide his panic. "Um . . . Why, yes! Come in! Just let me get a pen."

As Thanatos ducked under the low doorway, Sisyphus grabbed the nearest heavy object he could find—a stone pestle he used to grind his flour—and smacked the god of death over the head.

Thanatos passed out cold. Sisyphus tied him up, gagged him, and stuffed him under the bed. When Mrs. Sisyphus came home, she was like, "Why is there a giant black wing sticking out from under the bed?"

Sisyphus explained what had happened. His wife wasn't pleased.

"This is going to get us both into trouble," she said. "You should have just died."

"I love you, too," Sisyphus muttered. "It'll be fine. You'll see."

It wasn't fine. Without Thanatos on the job, people stopped dying. At first, nobody objected. If you were supposed to die and you didn't, why would you complain?

Then a big battle happened between two Greek cities, and Ares, the god of war, got suspicious. He hovered over the battlefield like he always did, ready for an exciting day of carnage. When the two armies clashed, no soldiers fell. They just kept whaling on each other, hacking each other to bits. Things got messy, with plenty of blood and gore, but no one died.

"Where's Death?" Ares screamed. "This is no fun without Death!"

He flew from the battlefield and started asking all around the world: "Excuse me, have you seen Death? Big guy with black feathery wings? Likes to reap souls?"

Finally somebody mentioned that they'd seen a guy like that heading toward old man Sisyphus's house.

Ares broke down Sisyphus's front door. He pushed the old dude aside and spotted Thanatos's left wing sticking out from under the bed. Ares pulled out the god of death, brushed off the dust bunnies, and cut his bonds. Then both gods glared at Sisyphus.

Sisyphus backed into the corner. "Um, look, guys, I can explain—"

BOOM!

Ares and Thanatos vaporized him with a double blast of godly wrath.

Once Sisyphus's soul found its way to the Underworld, Sisyphus somehow managed to get an audience with Hades himself.

The old man bowed before the god's throne. "Lord Hades, I know I did a bad thing. I'm ready to face my punishment. But my wife! She didn't do the proper funeral rites for me! How can I enjoy eternal damnation knowing that the missus didn't honor the gods with sacrifices as you have commanded? Please, just allow me to return to the world long enough to scold my wife. I'll come straight back."

Hades frowned. Of course he was suspicious, but he'd always been under the impression that spirits couldn't lie. (He was wrong.) Also, Sisyphus's story filled him with outrage. Hades hated it when people didn't take funeral rites seriously. And sacrifices to the gods? Those were even *more* important!

"Fine," Hades said. "Go scold your wife, but don't take too long. When you get back, I'll have a special punishment ready for you."

"I can't wait!" Sisyphus said.

So his spirit returned to the world. He found his vaporized

remains and somehow got them back together into a regular body. You can imagine his wife's surprise when Sisyphus walked in the front door, alive as ever. "Honey, I'm home!"

After his wife woke up from fainting, Sisyphus told her the story of how he cleverly escaped death yet again.

His wife was not amused. "You can't cheat Hades forever," she warned. "You're asking for trouble."

"I've already been condemned to the Fields of Punishment," Sisyphus said. "What do I have to lose? Besides, Hades is busy. He sees thousands of souls every day. He won't even know I'm gone."

For years, Sisyphus's plan actually worked. He kept a low profile. He stayed at home most of the time, and when he had to go out, he wore a fake beard. Hades *was* busy. He forgot all about Sisyphus, until one day Thanatos happened to ask: "Hey, what'd you ever do to that creep who stuffed me under his bed?"

"Oh . . ." Hades frowned. "Whoops."

This time, Hades sent the messenger god Hermes to look for Sisyphus. Hermes wore a helmet, so he couldn't get whacked over the head so easily. The messenger god dragged Sisyphus back to the Underworld and threw him at the foot of Hades's throne.

Hades smiled coldly. "Lie to *me*, will you? Oh, I have something *very* special for you!"

He took Sisyphus to the middle of the Fields of Punishment, to a barren hill five hundred feet high with sides that sloped at forty-five degrees, just perfect for skateboarding. At the bottom of the hill sat a big round boulder the size of a compact car.

"Here you are," Hades said. "As soon as you manage to push this rock to the top of that hill, you can go. Your punishment will be over."

Sisyphus sighed with relief. He'd been expecting much worse. Sure, the boulder looked heavy. Pushing it up the hill would suck, but at least it wouldn't be impossible.

"Thank you, Lord Hades," Sisyphus said. "You are merciful."

"Right." Hades's dark eyes glinted. "Merciful."

The god disappeared in a cloud of gloom, and Sisyphus got to work.

Unfortunately, he soon found out his job *was* impossible. Pushing the rock took every bit of his strength, and as soon as Sisyphus got close to the top of the hill, he lost control. No matter what he tried, the boulder would roll back to the bottom. Or it would run over him and *then* roll to the bottom.

If Sisyphus stopped to rest, one of the Furies came along and whipped him until he got moving again. Sisyphus was doomed to roll his rock uphill for eternity, never reaching the top.

Another happy ending! Ares, the god of war, got to watch people die again. Mrs. Sisyphus got some peace and quiet. And Thanatos, the god of death, decided not to ring anyone's doorbell and require a signature anymore. From then on, he just sneaked around invisibly and took his victims' souls without warning. So if you were planning on living forever by tying up the god of death and stuffing him under your bed, you're out of luck.

So that's how Hades got the Underworld organized. He built his dark palace on the edge of the Fields of Asphodel, and once he married Persephone, he more or less settled down and was about as happy as an Underworld god can be.

He started raising a herd of black cattle so that he could have fresh steak and milk, and he appointed a daimon named Menoetes to look after the cows. Hades also planted an orchard of magical pomegranate trees to honor his wife.

The Olympian gods rarely visited—except for Hermes, who had to deliver messages and souls—but if you happened to be in Hades's throne room on any given day, you might find Thanatos hanging out, or the Furies, or the three dead-celebrity judges. The best deceased artists and musicians from Elysium were often summoned to the palace to entertain the king.

Were Persephone and Hades a happy couple? Hard to say. The old stories aren't even clear about whether they had any children. Apparently Persephone had a daughter named Melinoe, who was the daimon in charge of ghosts and night-mares, but Hades may or may not have been the father. Some stories say the father was actually Zeus *disguised* as Hades, which gets us into a whole new level of gross.

A few poems mention Makaria, the daughter of Hades and Persephone. She was the goddess of blessed peaceful deaths, as opposed to painful, terrible, horrifying deaths, but there aren't really any stories about her.

At any rate, Hades wasn't always faithful to Persephone. He's a god. What did you expect?

One time Hades was visiting the Titan Oceanus at the bottom of the sea. What he was doing there, I have no idea. Maybe he was checking on the salty springs that fed the River Styx. Anyway, while he was roaming around, he happened to meet a beautiful ocean nymph named Leuke, one of Oceanus's daughters. She was tall and pale and lovely, and apparently she made a big impression. At the end of the visit, Hades abducted her and took her back to the Underworld.

It was just a fling, a momentary madness, but you can guess how Persephone reacted when she found out her husband had brought a souvenir girl home with him.

"She goes or I go," Persephone snarled. "And don't just send her back to the ocean. She stole my husband! She must die!"

"Um . . . okay," Hades said. "I mean, yes! Of course, dear! What was I thinking?"

Hades ran down to the Fields of Asphodel, where Leuke was waiting for him.

"Well?" Leuke demanded. "You abducted me and brought me here. What do you plan to do with me?"

"Actually, it's not going to work out," Hades said. "My wife doesn't approve."

"What a shocker," Leuke muttered. "Fine. Take me home!"

"I can't," Hades said. "Persephone wants you dead."

Leuke turned even paler. "That—that isn't right! You stole *me!*"

"It's okay," Hades assured her. "I have an idea. Instead of killing you, I'll just change you into something—like a plant. Then you'll live forever, and I can always remember you."

"That's a horrible idea!"

"Maybe a tree," Hades mused.

"No!"

"A tall, pale, white tree," Hades decided. "A tree as beautiful as you are."

"I—"

POOF.

Leuke became the first poplar tree, and Hades hugged her trunk. "Thanks for understanding. I will always remember you."

The poplar quickly multiplied, until the Fields of Asphodel were dotted with them—a little bit of beauty in the gloomy fields of Asphodel. The poplar became one of Hades's sacred trees, and tended to grow especially thick along the banks of the Underworld rivers, maybe because Leuke remembered that she had come from the sea and was trying to grow her way back there. Good luck with that, Leuke.

After his failed romance with the poplar girl, Hades became depressed. One day he decided to take a long stroll along the River Cocytus, the River of Wailing, which is an odd place to walk if you're trying to cheer yourself up.

Hades happened to see a lovely young woman in a pale-green dress sitting by the water. Her fragrance wafted toward him on the subterranean breeze—a sweet, subtle perfume unlike anything he'd ever smelled.

He walked over and stared at her in amazement. Hades tended to surprise people, being so dark and stealthy and all; so when the girl finally noticed him, she flinched in alarm.

"What do you want?" she demanded.

"Uh . . ." Hades found it hard to think. The woman's eyes were pale green like her dress. "I'm Hades. You smell good. Who are you?"

The girl wrinkled her nose. "I'm Minthe, of course. Daughter of the River Cocytus."

Hades frowned. "The Underworld rivers have naiads? I never knew that."

"Well, maybe we're not proud of it," Minthe muttered.

"It's not easy being the nature spirit for a wailing river, you know. I'd much rather be in the upper world, where I could enjoy the sunlight and the fresh breeze."

"I'll take you there," Hades blurted. "Just give me a kiss, and I'll take you to the upper world."

Minthe knit her eyebrows. "Why would you?"

"I love you," Hades said foolishly, but he didn't meet many beautiful women. Also, it was springtime. Persephone had gone to visit her mother in the mortal world, and Hades was lonely.

Minthe stood. She wasn't sure what to think of this dark god, but a trip to the upper world sounded good. She said, "All right."

She kissed him. Hades put his arms around her, and together they dissolved into shadows.

They appeared on the side of a hill near the Greek town of Pylos. Minthe gasped when she saw the blue sky and the sun, the green hills marching on forever.

She smiled and threw her arms around Hades, and for about twenty seconds they were very much in love. Minthe's fragrance was intoxicating.

Then something changed. Hades tensed. Maybe the fresh air cleared his mind.

"What am I doing?" he wailed, pushing Minthe aside. "It's springtime. My wife will be around here somewhere, making plants grow and whatnot. She'll find us!"

"Who cares?" Minthe asked. "You said you loved me."

"I—I—" Hades gulped.

Minthe's green eyes were gorgeous. She was very pretty and she smelled good, but now Hades realized their love was hopeless. He remembered the murderous look in Persephone's eyes when she'd heard about Leuke.

"I've got to get back to Erebos," Hades said. "Enjoy the upper world."

"You're coming back, right?" Minthe demanded.

"Um . . ." Hades chickened out and dissolved into shadows.

Minthe should've forgotten him. She'd made it to the mortal world! She could've found a new river to bind her life force to. She could've lived forever in the beautiful forests and hills of Greece.

But nope. Too easy!

Being dumped on the hillside made her angry. It dawned on her that she'd wrapped the god Hades around her little finger without even trying. She really *must* be beautiful. And she did smell great. She deserved to be a queen.

"Hades loves *me!*" she shouted to the wind. "He's going to come back and get me and make *me* the queen of the Underworld! I am more beautiful than Persephone, and more wonderful, and I smell better, and—"

The hillside rumbled. Grass and flowers swirled into a massive funnel cloud of petals. The goddess Persephone appeared as a fifty-foot-tall colossus.

At that point, Minthe realized she'd made a mistake.

"YOU, PRETTIER THAN ME?" Persephone boomed. "YEAH, RIGHT! YOU DO SMELL GOOD, THOUGH. PERHAPS I CAN FIND A USE FOR YOU AMONG THE PLANTS!"

Persephone raised her giant sandaled foot and squashed Minthe flat. When she smeared her foot across the hillside, tiny green plants sprang up. Their leaves smelled wonderful whenever they were crushed. Persephone decided to call them *mint* plants, and the hill near Pylos where they first grew is still called Mount Minthe.

So next time you have mint chocolate chip ice cream, you can thank Persephone, though it can be a little hard to eat the stuff when you realize it's made from smashed river nymph.

After that, Hades didn't have many affairs. He mostly stayed in his palace and minded his own business.

Mortal heroes didn't always leave *him* alone, though. They kept popping down, demanding things. One hero wanted his dog, Cerberus. Another hero wanted Hades to return his dead sweetheart to life. Another hero even tried to abduct Persephone. Maybe I'll tell you those stories another time, but all this gloomy Underworld stuff is making me claustrophobic.

I need some fresh sea air. Let's pop over to the Mediterranean, and I'll introduce you to my dad—the one and only Poseidon.

POSEIDON GETS SALTY

I'M BIASED.

But if you're going to have a Greek god for a parent, you couldn't do better than Poseidon. Sure, I've had my problems with him. He's not the most attentive dad. But, hey, none of the Greek gods is.

At least Poseidon has awesome powers and a laid-back attitude (most of the time).

He's amazingly cool, considering how hard it was for him as a young god. He was the middle boy. He was always being compared to his brothers, like: *Wow, you're almost as handsome as Zeus! You're almost as powerful as Zeus!* Or sometimes: *You're not as much of a loser as Hades!*

That can really grate on a guy after a few centuries.

Back when Zeus, Poseidon, and Hades threw dice to divide up the world, Poseidon got the *second*-best roll. He had to accept his brother Zeus's becoming lord of the universe and telling him what to do for all eternity, but Poseidon didn't complain. He'd won the sea. That was fine with him. He liked the beach. He liked swimming. He liked seafood.

True, Poseidon wasn't as flashy or powerful as Zeus. He didn't have lightning bolts, which were like the nuclear arsenal of Mount Olympus. But Poseidon *did* have his magical trident. He could stir up hurricanes, summon tidal waves, and make a *mean* smoothie. Since the seas wrapped around the earth, Poseidon could also cause earthquakes. If he was in a bad mood, he could level whole cities or make islands sink beneath the waves.

The Greeks called him the Earthshaker, and they went to a lot of trouble to keep him happy, because no matter whether you were on land or at sea, you *didn't* want Poseidon mad at you.

Fortunately, Poseidon was usually calm. His mood reflected the Mediterranean Sea, where he lived, and most of the time the Mediterranean was smooth sailing. Poseidon would let the ships travel where they wanted. He'd bless fishermen with good catches. He'd chill on the beach, sip his umbrella drink from a coconut shell, and not sweat the small stuff.

On nice days, Poseidon would ride his golden chariot across the waves, pulled by a team of white hippocampi, which were horses with golden manes, bronze hooves, and fish tails. Everywhere he went, the sea creatures would come out to play around his chariot, so you'd see sharks and killer whales and giant squids all frolicking together, gurgling, "Hooray, Poseidon is in the house!" or whatever.

But sometimes the sea got angry, and Poseidon was the same way. When that happened, he was a totally different dude. If you were a ship's captain and you forgot to sacrifice to

Poseidon before you set sail, you were a major-league derp. Poseidon liked at least one bull sacrificed in his honor per ship. Don't ask me why. Maybe at one point Poseidon had told the Greeks, *Just pour me a Red Bull and we'll call it even,* and the Greeks thought he wanted an actual red bull.

If you forgot to sacrifice, there was a good chance your ship would get smashed on the rocks, or eaten by a sea monster, or captured by pirates with bad personal hygiene.

Even if you never traveled by sea, that didn't mean you were safe. If your town somehow offended Poseidon . . . well, say hello to Hurricane Derp.

Still, Poseidon kept it together most of the time. He tried to follow Zeus's orders, though Zeus annoyed him constantly. Whenever those two started arguing, the other gods buckled their seat belts, because a fight between the sky and the sea could rip the world apart.

Mother Rhea must've sensed the tension early on. Shortly after the gods took over the world, she suggested that Poseidon get out of Olympus and explore his new domain. She sent him to live on the ocean floor with a tribe of aquatic weirdos called the *telkhines.*

This was a strange suggestion, since the telkhines were twisted little dudes. They'd once been land dwellers, until they did something to anger Zeus; so he tossed the worst ones into Tartarus and exiled the rest to the bottom of the sea.

What did they do? Not sure; but the telkhines were known for sorcery and crafting dangerous stuff. They could summon sleet, rain, or even snow (which you don't get much in Greece), and call down sulfurous rain that destroyed plants and burned flesh, which was kind of cool in a gross, smelly way.

Some stories say that the telkhines invented metalworking, and even made Kronos's scythe at Gaea's request. Could be true. They were greedy, and would do anything for the right price.

After Zeus threw them into the ocean, their forms changed so that they looked like a cross between dogs, seals, and humans, with canine faces, stunted little legs, and half-flipper hands that were nimble enough for metalwork but still made great Ping-Pong paddles.

When Poseidon came to live with them, the telkhines showed him around and taught him the ways of the ocean: *These are fish! This is coral!* One especially nasty trick they taught him was how to use his trident as a lever. Poseidon learned how to wedge the trident's points under the base of an island and flip it so that the whole landmass disappeared under the sea. In combat, he could do this with mountains on dry land. A couple of times he flipped mountains right on top of his enemies, crushing them flat. See, I told you he was a boss.

Eventually, Poseidon got tired of the telkhines and decided to build his own palace. *(Good move, Dad.)*

He went to the bottom of the Aegean Sea and used his earthshaking, wave-making powers to raise a big mansion made of pearl, sea stone, and abalone shell. His gardens were full of exotic sea plants, with luminescent jellyfish drifting around like Christmas lights. He had great white sharks for guard dogs and mermen for servants; and his doorways were huge, because every once in a while the whales and sea monsters would float through to pay their respects.

If you ask me, Poseidon's crib was *way* cooler than Hades's or Zeus's, and when Poseidon was sitting on his polished coral throne, he felt pretty good about himself. The entire sea was under his control. The fish adored him. All the sailors in the Mediterranean made offerings to him and prayed for safe passage. Everybody seemed to love him.

So Poseidon thought, Hey, I should go up top and offer to be the patron for one of the mortal cities!

Like I mentioned earlier, this was a big deal for gods. The more mortals who prayed to you, the stronger you got. If you could get a whole city dedicated to you—with statues, and temples, and souvenir T-shirts in all the tourist shops—that was the ultimate in bragging rights.

Poseidon decided to try for the capital of Attica on the Greek mainland, which was one of the biggest and most important cities in Greece. Hey, go big or go home, right?

He showed up at the city's acropolis, which was the main fortress on the top of the tallest hill. The earth shook. Poseidon appeared in a swirling column of salt and mist. He struck his trident against the nearest rock, splitting it open and creating a geyser of salt water.

"Behold!" he shouted to the crowds. "I am Poseidon, here to become patron of your city!"

Pretty good entrance. Unfortunately, Athena, the goddess of wisdom, had shown up a few seconds before with the exact same offer. She was standing nearby in her gray robes, her battle helmet tucked under her arm, conducting negotiations with the city elders.

"Ah," Poseidon muttered. "Awkward."

The city elders gaped at the sea god with his glowing trident, and at the massive geyser of salt water that now spouted from the hilltop.

"Lord Poseidon!" one said. "Oh . . . um . . ."

The poor mortals looked back and forth between the two gods. I can't blame them for being nervous. You never want to be forced to choose between gods. No matter which you pick, the other one is likely to stomp you as if you were a cockroach.

Poseidon wasn't sure what to do either. How dare this upstart goddess Athena, this second-generation Olympian, steal his idea? He was tempted to chase her off with his trident; but before he could, Athena cried, "I know how we can settle this peacefully!"

Typical. Athena *always* had some sneaky idea. Poseidon wasn't interested in peace at the moment, but the mortals all looked very relieved, and he didn't want to act like a bad sport in front of his future followers.

"Well?" he grumbled. "What is your plan?"

"A contest," Athena said. "You and I will each create one gift for the city. The elders will judge between them. Whichever god gives the city the most *valuable* gift will be its patron. The other god will accept the elders' judgment and leave in peace. Agreed?"

Thousands of mortal eyes turned to Poseidon. He still wanted to smack Athena into the sea, but she had put him on the spot. He couldn't exactly say no.

"Yeah," he grunted. "Okay."

Athena gestured to him courteously. "Gentlemen first."

Poseidon frowned. What would be a valuable gift for these mortals? A box of pearls? Some pet jellyfish? Perhaps a stable of trained whales they could ride? Hmm. Parking the whales downtown might be a problem.

Perhaps another form of animal . . . something strong and fast, but adapted to land-dwelling humans?

Poseidon gazed at the waves breaking on the beach far below. As the whitecaps raced and crashed, he got an idea. He began to smile.

"Watch this," he said.

He pointed his trident, and the waves began to take shape. When they reached the shore, they became majestic animals with four long legs and flowing manes. They ran straight onto the beach, whinnying and prancing.

"I call them *horses!*" Poseidon shouted. "They are fast and strong. You can ride them anywhere. They carry heavy stuff, pull plows or wagons. You can even ride them into war and trample your enemies. Plus, they just look really cool."

The mortals murmured and clapped politely. Horses were obviously a valuable gift, though a few of the townspeople looked disappointed, like maybe they'd been hoping for pet jellyfish.

Everyone turned to Athena.

The goddess raised her hand. A sickly-looking shrub broke through the nearby rocks. It had gray-green leaves and green knobby fruits the size of warts.

Poseidon couldn't help laughing. "What the spume is that?"

"It's an olive tree," Athena said.

The mortals shifted uneasily. The olive tree didn't look very impressive, but nobody wanted to say that to Athena.

Poseidon chuckled. "Okay, well, nice try. I guess we know who won *this* contest!"

"Not so fast," Athena said. "The olive tree may not look like much, but you can grow it with very little effort. It will spread across the countryside until olives are the most important food in Greece."

"Those knobby black things?" Poseidon protested. "They're tiny!"

"But they will grow by the thousands," Athena said. "And they're tasty on pizza! The mortals of this city will export olives across the world and become rich! You can use olive oil for cooking and lighting lamps. You can even add perfume to the oil and use it for bathing, or moisturizing, or cleaning those hard-to-get-out stains on your kitchen counters."

She turned to the crowd of mortals. "How much would you pay for it now? But don't answer! It's my gift to you, free of charge. And if you order today, you'll also get my patronage for your city, which includes tons of wisdom, advice about warfare, and all sorts of helpful crafts. You will be the richest and most important city in Greece! All I ask is that you name your city after me and build me a temple, which can be done in three easy installments."

Poseidon's confidence started to crumble. "But wait . . . my horses . . ."

The mortals were no longer listening. They were much more interested in making money, and while the countryside around their city was great for growing olives, it was too hilly and rocky for horses to be much use.

It was kind of ironic. The people of the city would eventually become famous sea traders, exporting their olive oil; but they turned down the sea god Poseidon's patronage. He might've done better if he'd offered them trained whales.

So Athena won the contest, and that's why the city is named Athens, after her, when it could have been named something cool like Poseidonopolis.

Poseidon stormed off, literally. He forgot his promise not to take revenge and almost destroyed the lower part of the city with a huge flood, until finally the Athenians agreed to build a temple on the acropolis honoring both Athena *and* Poseidon.

The temple is still there. If you go, you can see the marks left by Poseidon's trident where he struck the rock to make the saltwater spring. There are probably still olive trees around, too. But I doubt you'll see any horses.

After that, Poseidon got a little obsessed with finding a city to sponsor, but he didn't have any luck. He fought with Hera for the city of Argos. Hera won. He fought with Zeus for the island of Aegina. Zeus won. He fought with Helios for the city of Corinth and almost won, but Zeus said, "No, you guys split it. Helios, you can have the main city and the acropolis. Poseidon—you see that little skinny strip of land next to the city? You can have that."

Poseidon just kept getting shafted—or lightning-bolted, or olive-treed. The more times it happened, the crankier he got.

This was bad, because when Poseidon got touchy, he was more likely to punish whoever he thought was insulting him.

For instance, he was very proud of these fifty sea spirits called the Nereids, whose beauty was known throughout the world. They had long, flowing hair as dark as midnight, sea-green eyes, and gossamer white dresses that billowed around them in the water. Everyone knew they were absolute knock-outs, and having them in *his* domain was something that delighted Poseidon, kind of like living in a town with a championship football team.

Anyway, this mortal queen named Cassiopeia down in North Africa—she started bragging about how she was *way* more beautiful than the Nereids.

Poseidon had no patience for that nonsense. He summoned up a flesh-eating, blood-drinking sea serpent about a thousand feet long, with a mouth that could swallow a mountain, and he sent it to terrorize the coast of Africa. The monster raged up and down, devouring ships, making waves that sank villages, and bellowing so loudly no one could get any sleep.

Finally, to stop the attacks, Cassiopeia agreed to sacrifice her own daughter, Andromeda, to the sea monster. Like, *Oh, yeah, my bad. I shouldn't have bragged. Here, you can kill my innocent daughter!*

In case you're worried, my dad didn't actually let that happen. He allowed a hero to rescue Andromeda and kill the sea monster (which is a whole other story), but even after Cassiopeia died, Poseidon never forgot her insult. He put her in the night sky as a constellation, and because she had lied about being more beautiful than the Nereids, she always appeared to be spinning backward.

She's a stupid-looking constellation, too.

After that, the Nereids were grateful to Poseidon for upholding their honor. Maybe that was his plan all along. You can't beat having fifty beautiful women thinking you're awesome.

Most of the Nereids would've been happy to marry Poseidon, but one Nereid avoided him, because she was shy and didn't ever want to get hitched. Naturally, *she* was the one who caught Poseidon's eye.

Her name was Amphitrite, and her idea of paradise was

living a quiet life at the bottom of the sea with no gods calling her up for dates or trying their cheesy pickup lines on her when she went to the underwater mall.

Unfortunately, Amphitrite was gorgeous. The more she tried to avoid the gods, the more they pursued her. Her black hair was pinned back in a net of pearls and silk. Her eyes were as dark as mocha. She had a kind smile and a beautiful laugh. Usually she dressed in a simple white gown, her only piece of jewelry a circlet of polished red crab claws across her brow—which doesn't strike me as very attractive, but I guess it was fashionable among the Nereids.

Poseidon tried everything to win her heart: saltwater taffy, a serenade of whale songs, a bouquet of sea cucumbers, a Portuguese man-of-war festooned with pretty red ribbons. Amphitrite refused all his advances. Whenever he got too close, she blushed and swam away.

Finally she got so spooked that she fled for good. Poseidon searched for her everywhere, with no luck. He began to think that he'd never see her again. His heart sank deeper than a navy submersible. He moped around his palace, crying like a humpback whale, confusing all the sea mammals, and giving the giant squids migraines.

Eventually the sea creatures elected this god named Delphin to go talk to Poseidon and see what was wrong. Delphin was the immortal king of dolphins and a good friend of the sea god's. What did Delphin look like? A dolphin. Duh.

So Delphin swam into the throne room and chattered in Dolphinese: "What's up, P-man? Why the face?"

"Oh, it's Amphitrite." Poseidon heaved a sigh. "I love her, but she ran away!"

"Huh." Delphin thought that was a pretty stupid reason to mope around. "You do realize there are forty-nine other Nereids, right?"

"I don't care!" Poseidon sobbed. "I want Amphitrite!"

"Yeah, well, that's a bummer," Delphin said. "Look, your moaning and groaning is messing up everybody's sonar. Just this morning two blue whales got in a head-on collision and backed up the Aegean morning commute for miles. So how about I find this lady Amphitrite and convince her to marry you?"

Poseidon's tears dried immediately, which was impressive since he was underwater. "You could do that for me?"

"I'm a dolphin," Delphin chattered. "I have a huge brain. Back soon."

It took Delphin a while, but he finally located Amphitrite at the western edge of the Mediterranean, near where the Titan Atlas held up the sky.

Amphitrite sat on a coral ledge, watching the sunset filter through the deep water and make rosy streaks in the seaweed forests. A sea bass lay in her open palm, all blissed out, because Amphitrite really had a way with fish. Normally I don't think of sea bass as cuddly, but they *loved* her.

Delphin could see why Poseidon liked her. She radiated a sort of kindness and gentleness that you don't see in a lot of immortals. Usually with gods, the longer they lived, the more they acted like spoiled children. Delphin wasn't sure why, but that whole thing about getting wiser as you got older? Not so much.

Delphin floated up to Amphitrite. "Hey, what's up?"

Amphitrite didn't try to flee. She had never felt threatened by Delphin, maybe because of his dolphin smile.